Aurora

The northern lights in mythology, history and science

Harald Falck-Ytter

Aurora

The northern lights
in mythology, history and science

Photographs by Torbjörn Lövgren

Floris Books
Anthroposophic Press

Translated by Robin Alexander

First published in German under the title
*Das Polarlicht. Nordlicht and Südlicht in mythischer,
naturwissenschaftlicher und apokalyptischer Sicht.*
by Verlag Freies Geistesleben, Stuttgart, 1983.
First published in English in 1985 by Floris Books, Edinburgh,
and by Anthroposophic Press, Spring Valley, New York.

British Library Cataloguing in Publication Data

Falck-Ytter, H.
    The Aurora: the northern lights in mythology,
history and science.
    1. Auroras
    I. Title.   II. Lövgren, Torbjörn
III. Polarlicht. *English*
    523.01'88768   QC971.

ISBN 0–86315–020–9 (Floris Books)

ISBN 0–88010–123–7 (Anthroposophic Press)

Reproduced, printed and bound in Great Britain by
Hazell Watson & Viney Limited,
Member of the BPCC Group,
Aylesbury, Bucks

Dedicated to Theodor Däubler (1876–1934)
the apocalyptic herald of the northern lights

Contents

References

The system used in this book cites author and year of publication, followed by volume (if necessary) and page. The full title and publication details are in the bibliography.

Acknowledgements

The photographer, Torbjörn Lövgren, for many years co-worker at the Geophysical Institute for Aurora Observations in Kiruna, Sweden, has from the start generously made his pictures available and has taken pictures specifically for this book (the series on progressive movement, Plates 12 & 13). The lithographs by the Dane, Harald Moltke 1871–1960), from the beginning of the century, are reproduced on account of their great artistic value and expressive mood. They were kindly given by the Danish Meteorological Institute in Copenhagen.

Chapter 8 concerning Theodor Däubler and his poetical work has been abridged in translation from the comprehensive German.

Picture acknowledgements

Torbjörn Lövgren (Geophysical Institute, Kiruna, Sweden), all plates, except plates 11 and 19. Dr L. A. Frank (Baader Planetarium Archive), Plate 11. Rüdiger Gerndt (Baader Planetarium Archive), Plate 19. Scott Polar Research Institute, Cambridge, England, page 32. High Altitude Observatory, Boulder, Colorado, Figures 16–18. G. van Biesbroeck, Figure 15. Widener Library, Harvard University, Cambridge, Mass., Figures 1, 3–8. Germanic National Museum, Nürnberg, Figure 2. Theodor Däubler Archive, Berlin, Figure 22. Schiller National Museum, Marbach, West Germany, Figure 21.

1. The Aurora

*So blossoms from star to star
a jubilant salutation.*
                    Theodor Däubler

The phenomenon of the little-known, mysterious aurora appears in the sparsely populated polar regions of the north during the dark season of the year. Aurora borealis — in Greek, dawn of the North — is the scientific name of this colourful light-phenomenon in the Northern hemisphere; the corresponding phenomenon in the Southern hemisphere is called the southern dawn, aurora australis.

A closer observation of these natural phenomena and the ideas concerning them signified a new discovery for humanity in the nineteenth century. This was linked to the advance of explorers and adventurers into the uninhabited Arctic and Antarctic regions. What had been an everyday, self-evident experience for Eskimos, Lapps and other primitive folk throughout the centuries became a fascinating and revolutionary discovery for the scientifically minded peoples of Western culture. For, in the sunless darkness of the northern and southern night, a hitherto unseen light glowed before their eyes, divulging veils of colour which, in their intensity and transparency, had never been found anywhere else on earth. They resembled nothing ever seen on earth, except perhaps in dreams. Because this phenomenon was beyond the grasp of thought it was a long time before it could be understood how this light and colour could arise without the presence of sunlight. Flowing light and wafting colour — this remained a profound mystery to man's mind and eye. Numerous theories and hypotheses were put forward concerning the polar lights, only to be refuted or carried to absurdity. Only when the twentieth century brought a wider view of the cosmos was it possible to penetrate this mystery so far that the human spirit was led to a threshold where, unexpectedly, new clarifications of the mystery appear.

The first exact, modern accounts of the aurora were due to the courageous self-sacrificing discoveries of the nineteenth and early twentieth centuries. One of the most distinguished exponents of the northern lights was the Norwegian polar explorer and later diplomat, Fridtjof Nansen (1861–1930). Again and again he tried to portray the strange moving phenomenon of the aurora borealis in words, and in drawings. In his diary he wrote during the drift of *Fram* into the Arctic pack-ice (1904, 160):

> I try to find solace in a book; absorb myself in the learning of the Indians — their happy faith in transcendental powers, in the supernatural faculties of the soul, and in a future life. Oh, if one could only get hold of a little supernatural power now, and oblige the winds always to blow from the south!
>
> I went on deck this evening in a rather gloomy frame of mind, but was nailed to the spot the moment I got outside. There is the supernatural for you — the northern lights flashing in matchless power and beauty over the sky in all the colours of the rainbow! Seldom or never have I seen the colours so brilliant. The prevailing one at first was yellow, but that gradually flickered over to green, and then a sparkling ruby-red began to show at the bottom of the rays on the under side of the arch. And now from the far-away western horizon a fiery serpent writhed itself up over the sky, shining brighter and brighter as it came. It split into three, all brilliantly glittering. Then the colours changed. The serpent to the south turned almost ruby-red, with spots of yellow; the one in the middle yellow, and the one to the north, greenish white. Sheaves of rays swept along the side of the serpents, driven through the ether-like waves before a storm wind. They sway backward and forward, now strong, now fainter again. The serpents reached and passed the zenith. Though I was thinly dressed and shivering with cold, I could not tear myself away till

1. THE AURORA

the spectacle was over, and only a faintly glowing fiery
serpent near the eastern horizon showed where it had
begun. When I came on deck later the masses of light had
passed northward and spread themselves in incomplete
arches over the northern sky. If one wants to read mystic
meanings into the phenomena of nature, here, surely, is
the opportunity.

About a decade later there was a race for the South Pole. Roald
Amundsen (1872–1928), also a Norwegian polar explorer, landed on
the Ross Ice Shelf in the Antarctic in 1911. The British explorer,
Robert F. Scott (1868–1912), was also on his way to the South Pole.
In December 1911 Amundsen reached the South Pole, and was able
shortly after to return to his base camp without undue difficulty.
Robert Scott, too, reached the South Pole, but a month later. On
the return trek he and his companions were caught in a violent snow
storm. All died in the protracted icy storms in March 1912.

In Scott's personal notes, made during his preparations in the
Antarctic and published posthumously, there is, almost like a last
will and testament, a penetrating account of the aurora australis
(1927, 257):

The eastern sky was massed with swaying auroral light,
the most vivid and beautiful display that I had ever seen
— fold on fold the arches and curtains of vibrating
luminosity rose and spread across the sky, to slowly fade
and yet again spring to glowing life.

The brighter light seemed to flow, now to mass itself in
wreathing folds in one quarter, from which lustrous
streamers shot upward, and anon to run in waves through
the system of some dimmer figure as if to infuse new life
within it.

It is impossible to witness such a beautiful phenomenon
without a sense of awe, and yet this sentiment is not
inspired by its brilliancy but rather by its delicacy in light
and colour, its transparency, and above all by its
tremulous evanescence of form. There is no glittering
splendour to dazzle the eye, as has been too often
described; rather the appeal is to the imagination by the
suggestion of something wholly spiritual, something
instinct with a fluttering ethereal life, serenely confident yet
restlessly mobile.

One wonders why history does not tell us of 'aurora'

worshippers, so easily could the phenomenon be
considered the manifestation of 'god' or 'demon'. To the
little silent group which stood at gaze before such
enchantment it seemed profane to return to the mental and
physical atmosphere of our house.

To the attentive observer, the aurora appears ever and again as
something novel. The limitless diversity of its forms and waning
movement continually challenges one to describe and understand the
phenomenon anew. This was particularly so in times when
photography had not yet been developed. The first successful photograph of the polar lights was taken in the year 1892 by a German
physicist, Martin Brendal (1862–1939).

Prior to this event, in the days of adventurous wanderings on
foot, a modern Marco Polo travelled over wide areas of the earth as
a news correspondent, reporting his multifarious impressions in
detail. He was Bayard Taylor (1825–78), the American poet and
writer whose major work was a translation, with metrical fidelity,
of Goethe's *Faust*. Taylor saw the aurora borealis in northern Scandinavia and had the good fortune to see also a corona which appears
as a kind of epitome and culmination of the northern lights'
unfolding. In his book, which appeared in 1864 (63f) Bayard Taylor
writes:

> I opened my eyes, . . . looked upward, and saw a narrow
> belt or scarf of silver fire stretching directly across the
> zenith, with its loose, frayed ends slowly swaying to and
> fro down the slopes of the sky. Presently it began to
> waver, bending back and forth, sometimes slowly,
> sometimes with a quick, springing motion, as if testing its
> elasticity. Now it took the shape of a bow, now undulated
> into Hogarth's line of beauty, brightening and fading in
> its sinuous motion, and finally formed a shepherd's crook,
> the end of which suddenly began to separate and fall off,

*The Danish painter, Harald Moltke, accompanied various research
expeditions to Iceland and Finland in 1899 and 1900. At Akureyri, on the
Eyja Fjord, North Iceland (65.7 ° N) and at Utsjoki on the Tana river
in Finnish Lapland (69.9 ° N) he observed the aurora. He produced a set
of lithographs which still rank as the most significant artistic renderings of
the aurora. The following eight pictures are reproductions from this
collection.*

as if driven by a strong wind, until the whole belt shot away in long, drifting lines of fiery snow. It then gathered again into a dozen dancing fragments, which alternately advanced and retreated, shot hither and thither, against and across each other, blazed out in yellow and rosy gleams or paled again, playing a thousand fantastic pranks, as if guided by some wild whim.

We lay silent with upturned faces, watching this wonderful spectacle. Suddenly, the scattered lights ran together, as by a common impulse, joined their bright ends, twisted them through each other, and fell in a broad, luminous curtain straight downward through the air until its fringed hem swung apparently but a few yards over our heads. This phenomenon was so unexpected and startling, that for a moment I thought our faces would be touched by the skirts of the glorious drapery. It did not follow the spheric curve of the firmament, but hung plumb from the zenith, falling, apparently, millions of leagues through the air, its folds gathered together among the stars and its embroidery of flame sweeping the earth and shedding a pale, unearthly radiance over the waste of snow. A moment afterwards and it was again drawn up, parted, waved its flambeaux and shot its lances hither and thither, advancing and retreating as before. Anything so strange, so capricious, so wonderful, so gloriously beautiful, I scarcely hope to see again.

As a result of polar expeditions and travels in northern Scandinavia, exciting news of these natural phenomena penetrated Central Europe and America, where research workers attempted to explain them scientifically. To begin with, however, this met with no success at all. The nature and complexity of the phenomena proved too intricate for the level of thinking at that time. Thus, for many decades, a large number of unrelated individual observations were amassed which could be made coherent only through detailed work.

First, the dynamics of auroral movement were difficult to grasp. The beginning and end of a display were never discernible, nor could it be ascertained where and when the aurora would be seen in the sky. The moving, dramatic climax of an auroral appearance was characterized by a profusion of the most diversified forms imaginable, that could then disappear again unexpectedly. Arcs, bands, curtains, veils, drapery, rays and clouds could fill the dome of the

sky in continuous succession. With each later repetition of the aurora, everything was different. No known laws of cause and effect could cover this continual and unpredictable change of form. Even those best acquainted with the auroral phenomenon stood ever and again as if spellbound by the uniqueness and novelty of a major display.

In the first place, the enigma of the emergence of light and colour in the absolute darkness had a profoundly moving effect on the human soul. White light and the whole spectrum of the rainbow unfurled in an ever-fresh, colourful profusion. Out of a peaceful and soothing green an impulsive red would emerge from the spreading movement. Should a bright red polar light spread over the sky, a panic could grip the soul. Yellow rays, depths of blue and violet stirred up all kinds of emotion in the observer. No-one could explain where this exuberance of colour came from.

For a long time, there was controversy over the height at which the aurora was displayed. It was soon acknowledged that no human eye or even a trained ability to judge distance could estimate the unusual height and breadth of the source. And how low towards the earth the aurora reaches is not fully explained even today. At best, it could be assumed that the aurora is a meteorological phenomenon and therefore connected with air currents and weather — with cold and warmth or dampness and dryness.

Then the question arose: Where on the earth does the aurora appear? The further one moved north, or south, in different parts of the world, the clearer and more far-reaching the aurora was. However, it was then discovered, surprisingly enough, that the light and colour diminished significantly in the region of the poles and disappeared entirely in their immediate neighbourhood.

The view that the aurora is related to meteorological phenomena led to the search for a relationship with annual seasonal changes. But such a relationship was established only with difficulty. It was shown that the aurora can be visible only when, in the course of the day or year, darkness has fallen. When, therefore, in the northern Scandinavian summer, sunlight predominates, the aurora is not observable. Only when darkness descends again in the autumn, is the appearance of the aurora possible.

Following observations made over many decades, it was shown that, at least in northern Europe, there was a distinct diurnal auroral cycle. When, in what follows, a kind of archetypal development of the auroral phenomenon is described, one must emphasize that this

is the result of long attentive observation. For the vivacity and uniqueness of each individual major auroral display hinders, in the first instance, the perception of the prototype described.

First of all there is the homogenous *arc*. It runs usually from east to west across the whole sky, in northern Europe usually to the north. There are often several arcs. An arc is usually one to ten kilometres wide, whereas its length may stretch over a thousand kilometres. It is difficult for an observer to ascertain these dimensions visually because the lower edge of the aurora is most often at an altitude of over a hundred kilometres and the forms themselves are manifested several hundred kilometres above that. The distance of the aurora from the observer, therefore, generally amounts to several hundred kilometres.

At first, the arcs shine mostly as a white diffused light in which, apart from the form of the arcs themselves, no other configurations are yet present. The arcs are static to begin with and can remain so for several hours. They are most often visible in the early hours of the evening. Within the arcs a pulsing and flowing movement evolves. During the further development of the auroral display, the arc appears as a vertical structure of rays taking on a green or yellow-green colour. When the structure of rays begins to move, other colours appear, perhaps red. Seen close to, the individual rays are pleated curtains of light, vertically flowing curves of loosely folded, curtain-like *bands*. These appeared to a Russian cosmonaut flying through them in a space ship as an abundance of pillars of light. The initial amorphous arc is transformed into an incisive, pulsating pleated band. Only from a great distance does it appear as a structure of rays. With these vibrating folds, motion enters the coloured arc which now climbs up into the zenith. Should there be an increase in the vibrations of the folds, the band becomes a hanging *curtain*.

In the meantime, the activity of the aurora has increased considerably, as has also its exuberance of colour. The curtain-like band then forms the beginning of a second phase, often in the late evening. The movements of the band lead to overlapping vibrating motions of the arc, which may develop into spirals. A pulsating energy seizes the whole arched band, sets it into powerful vibration and begins to form fully free shapes. The band is thereby broken up and the independent forms fill large portions of the sky. Veils, curtains, spirals, drapery and rays produce a multifarious moving drama in the sky. The aurora has thus entered upon a third phase

of greatest activity, in which the whole vault of the heavens may flush red. Seen from the south, the various curtains and draperies usually hang slanting towards the centre of the northern lights. Seen from the north, or more precisely, from the regional centre of the northern lights, the curtains hang towards the observer. He can thus come to stand directly under the different and numerous curtains and draperies. They then all run vertically parallel. The effect of perspective thus brings into view a central point around which all the forms group themselves.

It is only with difficulty that the human eye can take in the spatial depth of these huge dimensions; hence the formations appear as though arranged round a middle point, allowing the image of a crown, called *corona*, to arise. A corona, too, takes on a very varying structure. The formation of this structure is the highest development of a third phase of the auroral phenomenon. Thereafter, the varied activity declines; individual fields of colour spread out like clouds over large parts of the sky, they may remain like this for about an hour. At this stage, there often arises a new arc.

However, in northern Scandinavia, there is, for the most part, a basic rhythm which runs from early evening until towards midnight; other regions present a different rhythm. The development of the individual phases here described may also take a quite different form; the above description is a kind of basic pattern that is seldom seen as such. Many researchers into the aurora do not, therefore, recognize such phases. The aurora evolves so arbitrarily and variably that it is difficult for the observer to perceive typical stages of development. And yet, already in the nineteenth century, there were accounts that quite clearly described such development without any consciousness of the archetypal form.

The Austrian polar scientist, Karl Weyprecht, (1838–81) led a research team to the Arctic Ocean in the years 1872 to 1874 and discovered the land which became known as Franz Josef Land after the then reigning Austrian Emperor. During the expedition, Captain Weyprecht experienced the aurora borealis, including a corona formation, and described it (Payer 1876):

> There in the south, low on the horizon, lies a faint arc of
> light. It looks as if it is the upper edge of the dark segment
> of a circle; only the stars that shine through it in
> untarnished brilliance convince us that the darkness of the
> segment is an illusion created by the contrast. Slowly, the
> arc increases in intensity and rises towards the zenith; it is

perfectly regular, both its ends almost touch the horizon and move out towards east and west the higher it rises. No rays are seen in it; the whole consists of a fairly homogeneous light substratum of magnificent, delicate colouring; it is a transparent white with a pale greenish shade, not dissimilar from the whitish green of a young plant which has sprouted without sunlight in the dark. The moon's light appears yellow beside this delicate colour, so pleasing to the eye, so beyond verbal description, and given by Nature only to the polar regions, the Cinderella of creation, as if by way of compensation.

The arc is broad; it is perhaps three times the breadth of the rainbow and its much sharper edges stand out glaringly against the deep darkness of the arctic night sky. Its light outshines the stars in unclouded brilliance. Higher and higher rises the arc, a classical calm lies over the whole phenomenon; only here and there does a wave of light dance across from one side to the other. Over the ice it grows lighter, individual clumps of ice are distinguishable.

It still stands at a distance from the zenith and already a second arc detaches itself from the dark segment to the south and by and by others follow it. They all climb towards the zenith, the first one has already crossed it and sinks slowly towards the northern horizon, losing its intensity. Now there are arcs of light spanning the whole of the heavens; seven are in the sky at the same time, but then their intensity is only low. The further they go towards the north, the paler they become, and finally they then disappear altogether; but, they often all return across the zenith and are extinguished as they come.

Only seldom, however, is the development of the northern lights so calm and regular.

In most cases, the schematic dark segment of the textbooks does not exist at all. At one or other side of the horizon there is a light bank of cloud; its upper edges are illuminated. From there a band of light develops, spreads out, increases in intensity and rises towards the zenith.

The colouring is the same as in the arcs, but the intensity of the light is stronger. In ever varying play, the band changes its position and configuration slowly, but without a break. It is broad, and its intensive white-green

stands out wonderfully against the dark background. Now it is entwined with itself in many spirals; but they do not conceal each other, the inner one is still clearly to be seen through the light of the others. Waves of light flit continually through the band in undulating movement throughout its extent. At one moment they are running from right to left, at another from left to right; they appear to cross over each other, depending upon whether they appear in front of or behind a spiral. Now the bend is coiled up along its whole length; it has arranged itself in graceful folds; it almost appears as though the wind, high up in the atmosphere, were pursuing a secret game with the wide flaming pennant whose end loses itself far away on the horizon.

The light grows ever more intensive; the waves of light follow one another ever faster; on the upper and lower edges of the band appear rainbow colours; the shining, delicate white in the middle is bordered by a narrow strip of red below, green above. In the meantime, out of one band two have merged; the upper one approaches ever nearer to the zenith, now rays begin to stream out in the direction of that point in the vicinity of the zenith towards which the south pole of a free-moving magnetic needle points. The band has almost reached it, and now, for a short time, there begins a magnificent display of rays centred on the magnetic pole, an indication of the intimate relationship of the whole phenomenon with our earth's mysterious magnetic forces.

The short rays glisten and flicker on all sides around the pole; prismatic colours are seen on all the edges, short and long rays alternate with one another, waves of light revolve round the centre in rapid alternation. What we see is the corona of the northern lights; it almost always appears when a band goes over the magnetic pole . . . However, the band is often revealed in a quite different form. Then it does not consist only of homogeneous light but of individual rays which, ranked close together, stand almost parallel towards the pole. A significantly greater intensity is evoked in every ray by each rapid succession of light waves; on this account, the individual rays appear to be in a continuous skipping motion; both edges, red and green,

dance wavelike up and down in tune with the traversing light waves.

Often, the rays are lengthened throughout the whole extent of the band, they reach up to the vicinity of the magnetic pole and appear to be almost fixed. They are sharply delineated but very much dimmer than the band itself and are not ranked close together. Their colour leans more to the yellow; it appears as though thousands of delicate golden threads are stretched in front of the heavens. Over the starry sky there then lies a magnificent veil of light, infinitely transparent; the threads of light out of which it is woven are sharply delineated against the dark background, its lower border is a wide intensive white band edged with the most delicate red and green and is in slow incessant motion in the most diverse folds and spirals. At the same time, a violent northern-light haze often lies at separate places in the sky.

. . . Yet another configuration. Throughout the day, bands of every possible form and intensity have cruised around in the sky; it is now eight o'clock in the evening, the hour of greatest auroral intensity. For the moment, there are only isolated pencils of rays in the sky; only in the south, close to the horizon lies a faint band that we hardly notice. All at once, it rises suddenly; it spreads out towards east and west; light waves begin to dance through; individual rays climb up towards the zenith. For a short time, it remains stationary, then it is suddenly animated. The waves of light run from east to west, the edges take on an intensive red and green, and dance up and down; the rays shoot faster into the heights, they become shorter; everything rises, nearer and nearer they come to the magnetic pole. Faster and faster the waves follow upon each other; they already tumble over one another, they cross each other, they run over each other; in a wild race the rays vie with one another to reach the pole first; but they are no longer individual rays — they are whole bundles that race simultaneously upwards into the whole southern heavens in a wild rush. And now they have all reached the point they all strove for and rays are shooting up and down in all directions, north and south, east and west.

Do the rays travel from above downwards or from

below upwards? Who can make the distinction? Around the
centre licks a sea of flames; is it red, white or green? Who
knows? All three colours are there at the same time. The
rays reach almost down to the horizon; the whole sky is
in flames.

The band has become an arc that runs over the pole and
arises on both sides of the horizon; it has become a fiery
river in which the broad light-waves rush with terrific speed
from one side to the other. Nature presents us with a
firework display whose magnificence surpasses the boldest
imagination. We listen instinctively; such an exhibition strikes
us as unthinkable without deafening noise; but a silent calm
reigns, not the slightest rustle reaches our ears. It has
grown bright over the ice. Yet already everything is fading.
With the same incomprehensible speed with which it came
it has disappeared again. Only there in the northern sky a
band now stands; the light-waves dance slowly through;
across the ice the dark night has again wrapped everything
in its cloak.

That was the aurora of the coming storm, the northern
lights in full glory. No colour and no brush is able to
paint it; no words can describe it in all its grandeur.

In the selected pictures of this book, an attempt has been made
to reproduce this archetypal development, firstly in lithographs by
the Danish painter, Harald Moltke (1871–1960), then in the series of
photographs by the Swede, Torbjörn Lövgren.

The behaviour of the aurora in different regions and at different
times is not yet fully explained. Past accounts often spoke of an
aurora that reached down to the earth's surface. The exact measurements now possible have not been able to confirm such nearness to
the earth. Despite this, descriptions of the aurora's immediate close-
ness to the earth are continually turning up. Thus Dorothy J. Ray
(1958, 17) writes:

The aurora never has been measured closer to the earth than
35 miles [55 km], and there is doubt whether it actually
gets that close. But dozens of lonely northerners have
watched their only guest, the aurora, wrap a mountain
with its flimsy nets. I have too, scientists to the contrary.

The Brooks Range in Alaska one night in late August
was as bright with the aurora as if it were dawn. After
two years in the North I had learned to view these dazzling

displays with equanimity, but this one differed from others as much as hamburger from a T-bone steak. The aurora had just accomplished the impossible. It had come down to meet the earth just a few miles from me. The top of the highest mountain in the vicinity, almost 9000 feet [2700 m] of vertical rock, was completely submerged in an auroral gauze.

When it lifted a few seconds later, I assumed I had been the victim of an arctic mirage. But that contrary aurora flickered and dipped over and around the mountaintop for more than 20 minutes, settling now and then with uncanny precision on its pinnacle. What I had witnessed was impossible, according to science. The sensible explanation is that it was reflections of light on skitterish clouds, or some other atmospheric condition. Others who report similar experiences have no doubt seen the same kind of phenomenon.

Numerous traditions, particularly those of the Indians, Eskimos and Lapps, but also later accounts, tell how the northern lights are often accompanied by different low but nevertheless distinct sounds. It is a hissing, crackling and piping. No measurements with the most modern equipment have been able to certify this. For a long time it appeared as a completely unsolved problem. A large part of the acoustic concomitant phenomena could be explained psychologically: the intensive and grandiose light and colour display also evokes sounds in the observer's psyche and sense of hearing. They are subjective and heard only inwardly. Nevertheless, a portion of the many descriptions points to an outer objective phenomenon.

Though the perception of sound was simultaneous with the auroral display, thoughtful consideration concludes that the sound could not come from the display. At the average height of the aurora's origin (over 100 km, 60 miles) hardly any sound arises, and should it take place at a significantly lower level the distance would still be so great that a simultaneous occurrence of light and sound could not be experienced; the latter would need some time to bridge the distance, very much longer than the time lapse between a flash of lightning and the following peal of thunder. Recently, attention has been drawn to electromagnetic tensions that are discharged over the surface of a landscape. These can be measured but are also demonstrated, for instance in northern Canada, on dogs whose hair stands on end and gives off crackling sparks in the presence of a

strong auroral light: As auroral displays are related to tensions in the earth's electric field, the discharge of such tensions could give rise, in certain regions, to acoustic phenomena similar to the crackling below high-tension pylon cables.

However, it is also assumed that the character of the aurora has changed fundamentally, compared with earlier phenomena. This view is poignantly expressed in a statement by the great German world traveller and researcher, Alexander von Humboldt (1769–1859): 'The northern lights appear to have become less noisy since their appearance has been more precisely registered.'

Woodcut by Frijdtof Nansen from an observation on November 28, 1893.

2. Aurora and mythopoeic consciousness

The Canadian Indians in the region around Ottawa, Ontario, possess a living tradition about the origin of the northern lights (Hamilton 1903, 16, 231):

> The demigod Nanahboozho created the world and human beings. After the creation was complete and people had received knowledge and experience in managing their environment, Nanahboozho passed on to his permanent abode in the North. But before he left mankind, he promised to look after them and follow their lives. As a sign of his protection he would from time to time light great flares whose reflection would be visible to mankind in the skies.

For the Ottawa Indians, the northern lights were reflections of Nanahboozho's flames which were experienced as a continually active, living reverberation of the creation; they are in the earth's circumference and do not intervene directly in actual nature.

This Indian tradition clearly expresses how the northern lights are a flaming image — witness to the creative forces — a witness that today still manifests the infinite diversity of the creative processes. From this point of view, the tradition of the Ottawa Indians is understandable and obvious. Other Indians experienced rather the mediating role of the northern lights. They are like an emissary and can take up a personal relationship. An Indian in the far North-West of Canada narrates (Gromnica 1971, 18, 44):

2. MYTHOPOEIC CONSCIOUSNESS

When I was a boy, people respected the northern lights as messengers of our spirits. People also said that some men and women can bring the northern lights down and make them obey their commands. You only have to walk outside, rub your hands together and whistle, then the northern lights will come down and sing and dance for you. When I was a young man I tried it once and it worked.

This personal approachability of the aurora borealis is mentioned in many accounts. Although the aurora in its isolated great height is very distant from humanity, it appears, ever and again, to lend its ear to human beings, hence its character as an emissary.

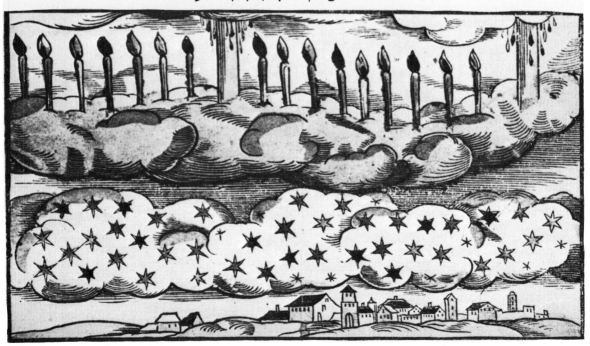

Figure 1. An early attempt to portray the aurora as seen in Bohemia in 1570.

A conception connected with the aurora that is often handed down is its relationship to unborn souls and children about to be born. One of the oldest traditions comes from ancient China about the year 2600 BC: 'The mother of the Yellow Emperor, Shuan-Yuan, Fu Pao, saw a big lightning circulating around the Su star of Bei-Don (Ursa Major α), with the light shining all over the field. She then became pregnant.' (Wang, Siscoe 1979, 40). Several elements in the account point to the aurora. The star mentioned is situated in the north. During a thunderstorm no stars are to be seen because the clouds cover them. The term lightning is used as a substitute or metaphor for northern lights. Furthermore, a lightning flash does not move in circles.

The influence of the aurora in the sphere of birth is often emphasized among other peoples. Thus a Siberian native tribe, the Chuvasch, have a god called Suratan-Tura which means, more or less, 'the heaven-sent birth.' The same name was used also for the northern lights and when they appear in the sky then, according to the Chuvasch tribe, a son will be born to Suratan-Tura. They also believed that women in childbirth would experience relief through the northern lights (Macculloch 1927, 4, 10). Even children playing would often be seen in the image of the aurora.

By far the most common, however, is the widespread idea that the dead are present in the aurora borealis, an idea that is portrayed in many different ways. An example of this is a tradition from the Eskimos in Labrador (Hawkes 1916, 153):

> The ends of the land and sea are bounded by an immense
> abyss, over which a narrow and dangerous pathway leads
> to the heavenly regions. The sky is a great dome of hard
> material arched over the earth. There is a hole in it
> through which the spirits pass to the true heavens. Only the
> spirits of those who have died a voluntary or violent
> death, and the raven, have been over this pathway. The
> spirits who live there light torches to guide the feet of new
> arrivals. This is the light of the aurora. They can be seen
> there feasting and playing football with a walrus skull.

Plate 1. The auroral arcs, while taking form, proceed from east to west. The lower edges of the arcs are in general sharply outlined; the upper edges dissolve away. When they come into movement, stronger colours arise. Through these movements the arcs can penetrate further towards the zenith.

2. MYTHOPOEIC CONSCIOUSNESS

The whistling crackling noise which sometimes
accompanies the aurora is the voices of these spirits trying
to communicate with the people of the earth. They should
always be answered in a whispering voice. Youths and
small boys dance to the aurora. The heavenly spirits are
called *selamiut*, 'sky-dwellers,' those who live in the sky.

In this tradition, it is worthy of note that not all deceased are to
be seen in the auroral sphere. These particular deceased are involved
in an activity: they help the new arrivals. The ball-game motif is
common and corresponds to the desire to make the aurora's dynamic
movements into a perceptual image.

The great Danish Greenland-explorer Knud Rasmussen
(1879–1933) collected traditions of the Igluik Eskimos in Greenland
that recount something similar to that of the Labrador Eskimos
(1932, 95):

The dead suffer no hardship, wherever they may go, but
most prefer nevertheless to dwell in the Land of Day,
where the pleasures appear to be without limit. Here, they
are constantly playing ball, the Eskimos' favourite game,
laughing and singing, and the ball they play with is the
skull of a walrus. The object is to kick the skull in such
a manner that it always falls with the tusks downwards, and
thus sticks fast in the ground. It is this ball game of the
departed souls that appears as the aurora borealis, and is
heard as a whistling, rustling, crackling sound. The noise
is made by the souls as they run across the frost-hardened
snow of the heavens. If one happens to be out alone at
night when the aurora borealis is visible, and hears this
whistling sound, one has only to whistle in return and the
light will come nearer, out of curiosity.

Accounts of both life and death are also interwoven in the aurora
traditions. In a narrative of the Skolt Lapps in North Finland both
these elements are seen together. The contemporary promoter of and
researcher into the culture of these Lapps, Robert Crottet, has retold
a story in this connection. The gist of it is: Although it is summer,

*Plate 2. After the initial white colour-phase the arcs often display shades of
yellow and green. This green is the basic colour of the aurora; the white of
the aurora, appearing repeatedly, bathes the whole landscape in a light
resembling clear moonshine.*

the dark hut of the oldest man in Lapland is illuminated by a lamp filled with light from the aurora. The old man held three rays of the northern lights prisoner in a bottle. They are three deceased souls who would rather live imprisoned on earth than free in heaven. A youth has followed the old man. Both are now in the old man's hut, and the youth perceives that he is locked in. With the help of the deceased souls, the old man wants to transfer the youth's soul into his own old body. He will thereby continue to live for he is already almost two thousand years old. As the deceased are freed from the bottle and plunge their hands into the youth's body, the northern lights from heaven descend onto the earth — despite the midnight sun's presence — 'suddenly, a gigantic blaze of light flames over the sky. The northern lights spread out their rays as though a huge flower had opened its petals. One of its petals rushes through the hut window. Then the hands are pulled back out of the youth's breast. He gives vent to a cry of joy.'

The northern lights thus took back to themselves the three dead souls and freed the youth. When he talked about his experience, no-one would believe him. Therefore the youth said to his fiancée, 'How is it, then, that you believe that the dead protect us in the northern lights?'

The content of this tradition reveals a peculiar situation: the northern lights, that have been forced down to earth have power to carry out a complicated vital process. Here, the motif is the conservation of life through an exchange of souls. At the same time, however, the power of the northern lights to penetrate the bright daylight is revealed in a surprising manner: it is always present, even in summer, and can hinder the dark practices of human beings. In this way, the auroral forces are projected into the terrestrial polarity of good and evil.

One of the most impressive traditions is to be found among the American Indians of the Pacific North West coast. They tell how a particular person manages to penetrate the strange realm of the northern lights, to have experiences there, and to return to earth. These Indians narrate (Judson 1920, 143–5):

> Chief M'Sartto, Morning Star, had an only son, different from all others in the tribe. The son would not play with other children but would take his bow and arrow and be away for days. Curious as to what mischief his boy could be up to, the Chief one day followed him. His journey progressed and all at once a queer feeling filled the old

Chief, as if all knowledge was floating away from him. His eyes suddenly closed and when they were opened he found himself in an extremely light country with no sun, moon, or stars. There were many people about, and they spoke a strange language which he did not understand. The people were engaged in a wonderful game of ball which seemed to turn the light to many colors. The players all had lights on their heads and wore very curious belts called *Menquan*, or Rainbow belts. After many days of searching for his son, the old Chief met a man who spoke his language. The man had also traveled by chance to this strange new country and knew of the Chief's son. When he was brought to his son, the Chief saw him playing ball with the others, and strangely enough the boy's light was brighter than any there. When the game was ended, the old Chief was introduced to the people and honored by the Chief of the Northern Lights; two great birds were ordered to be brought forth, *K'che Sippe* by name. On these birds the

Figure 2. In Nuremberg, Germany, the aurora was seen in 1591 and in this engraving is portrayed as fire.

two dwellers of the Lower World returned home from the Wa-ba-ban, the land of the Northern Lights, following the Spirits Path, Ket-a-gus-wowt or Milky Way. Again all knowledge was erased from Chief M'Sartto. When they arrived home, the Chief's wife paid no notice that they were gone because she was afraid that they would never return and was very relieved. So it is that those very few who travel to the Land of the Northern Lights do not remember their remarkable journey. But the Chief's son remembers and travels there often.

In this calm, matter-of-fact narrative account there is a historical relationship to the soul-journeys of the north Asiatic shamans. Much more, there appears here an aspect of the future, when it will be possible for man to cross the threshold of birth and death consciously. This would happen in the light of an initiation that takes place in the symbolic realm of the aurora borealis.

The Greeks also knew of a legendary people who lived in northern Europe. They spoke of the Hyperboreans. The name means beyond the north (the north wind.) This far-northern people lived, like those inhabitants of the auroral world described by the Indians and Eskimos, in a mild, sunny and fertile land, free from the weight of earthly destiny. An age of a thousand years was assigned to these inhabitants; only when they tired of life did they die a quick and painless death. When the winter came in Greece, the sun-god Apollo moved to the land of the northern inhabitants in the land of Hyperborea. This mythical event presents a peculiar puzzle: Apollo, who is akin to light, moves into the darkness and cold of the northern polar night.

In the traditions of ancient clairvoyance and the mystery centres, the Greeks and their initiates did not, like modern man, see only the external darkness, nor did they experience only the physical cold of the terrestrial north. They experienced how this part of the earth is permeated by supersensory light-forces and occult heat-activity. Together with the outer sunlight, these forces are an essential element of Apollo's being. In the Hyperborean realm, supersensory light is transformed into visible illumination, occult heat into the external colour flow of the aurora.

It was, therefore, a spiritually perceived sequence of events to see Apollo during the dark season in that region of the earth where the supersensory sun-forces were just then appearing outwardly in the aurora borealis. In Southern Europe, in winter, the outward-turned activity of the sun is essentially at rest. In the north, in the old Hyperborea, it is roused and is active with the outward-streaming aurora.

The step from occult light-forces to life itself is but a small one. It is intimated in the birth-myths of the dweller in the far north, cited above. The phenomena of the active life-realm are fully represented in the *Kalevala* resuscitated by Elias Lönnrot (1802–84) in Finland, an epic of the Finno-Ugrian peoples. In the centre of this epic there is a mysterious thing: the Sampo. It is created by the divine-human smith Ilmarinen in dark Sariola, the land of the North. In the epic, it is said of the creation of the Sampo (X, 414–22):

> Forged with cunning art the Sampo,
> And on one side was a corn-mill,
> On another side a salt-mill
> And upon the third a coin-mill.
>   Now was grinding the new Sampo,
> And revolved the pictured cover,
> Chestfuls did it grind till evening,
> First for food it ground a chestful,
> And another ground for barter,
> And a third it ground for storage.

This miraculous entity not only grinds substances but also creates them. The sphere of life to which this pertains points to human beings: flour is generated by the living, it is nourishment for human beings and the foundation of daily bread. It leads towards the life-processes of the human physical body. Salt is taken from the mineral world and is a necessary addition to human nourishment; in human consciousness it works its way into the will-structure of the soul. The words of Christ 'You are the salt of the earth' (Matt.5:13) make clear this life-process in the soul. Coinage, as money, emphasizes life's interconnections in the human relationships created by the human spirit through work. These interconnections are the basis for new, spiritual activity. They are the life-processes of body, soul and spirit which are brought forth by the Sampo as it grinds.

This Sampo is roofed over by a many coloured lid which also revolves. In Finnish it is called: *Kirjokansi*. This word signifies the vault of the heavens. The same word is used later (XLVII, 110) for the heavenly spheres. A spark of fire falls 'through six spangled vaults of heaven': *Halki Kuuen Kirjokannen*. The word *Kansi* (*Kannen* is plural) is also contained in the Finnish word for the vault of the heavens: *Taivaankansi*. *Kirjo* means 'colourful, embroidered, rune and

41

Figure 3. Illustrations for an essay on the aurora which appeared in the Acta Societatis Hafniensis, Copenhagen, 1745. The endeavour was to portray the arc and ray structure of the aurora.

script.' Thus imaginatively developed, *Kirjokansi* could mean: the revolving vault of the heavens filled with brilliant stars and coloured northern lights, in which vault a numerous variety of runes and written signs and forms are visible. Whoever could interpret the 'many coloured lid' would be able to read the heavenly script. Below this lid lies the Sampo's nether part. What did these early peoples see in the Sampo?

The Finno-Ugrian peoples migrated in early prehistoric times from Russia's interior into the Baltic region to about latitude 60°. From the Baltic they could penetrate the North unhindered, settle along the coasts and also explore the far North. In the migrations from south to north and back again, these peoples discovered the threshold and limit of latitude 60°. At this latitude, the year begins to divide itself into uninterrupted light and dark halves. Here also, the rising northern lights take over from the fading sunlight in autumn. At this latitude, the frontier between the two mythical realms and lands of the *Kalevala* can be seen: Northland and Kalevala.

The content of the epic is the contentious drama in the relationships between the life-forces that takes place on this frontier. This is revealed in its global dimension when attention is directed to a still deeper-lying fact; an elemental-supersensory sheath of forces surrounding the earth dips down to the earth at this point. It does so by shifting its centre from the earth's centre somewhat in the direction of the sun. Sun-related life-processes emanate from this spherical sheath and are rhythmically formed by the earth's rotation. The elemental sphere of forces does not move with the earth, but remains in a kind of static relationship to the sun. The structure of its forces is able to influence the earth-elements so that, for example, it can give rise to fluctuations in atmospheric pressure. In this way a sort of friction is generated on the earth, a perpetual grinding between this sheath of forces and the earth's sphere.

It is in contemplation of these facts that myth merges with modern natural and spiritual science. To the old clairvoyance of the Finno-Ugrian peoples this planetary occurrence must have given rise to the impression of a mill-grinding image that is able to produce and treat life substances for human existence. The *Kalevala* calls this creation Sampo. Because an earthly human being cannot forthwith apprehend this image, and finds it even more difficult to acquire the life-forces, the Sampo had to be created by a divine-human creator. Gods and men had to fight in order to bring the Sampo south. As a consequence, it was broken in pieces and the largest piece sank in the sea. Nevertheless, splinters floating on the water contained the forces to create a new realm of life for human beings. This became the new land of Kalevala.

The *Kalevala* describes impressively, precisely and consistently how 'the many-coloured lid' is brought to the north again, either in bits or whole. For the present, it remains in the possession of the hostile Northland powers. The heavenly vault with the many coloured flaming northern lights still remains intact, but also unattainable, in the heights. A continuation of the epic would be the spiritual penetration of Sampo and the 'many coloured lid' and thereby the aurora borealis. A more precise account of the elemental-supersensory sphere of forces surrounding the earth will be given in Chapter 6.

3. The northern lights in history

The first certain and exact description of the northern lights appeared in the West in 467 BC. Plutarch (*c.* AD 46 – *c.*125), Greek philosopher and writer, says in his treatise on Lysander (12,4): 'for seventy-five days continuously there was seen in the heavens a fiery body of great extent, like a flaming cloud that did not rest in one place but moved along with intricate and regular movements so that through its darting and unsteady progress fiery fragments were broken off, and fiery flames were borne in all directions just like shooting stars.'

Many earlier accounts include descriptions that could refer to the aurora borealis. For instance, biblical passages have been quoted. However, in such cases, the nature of human consciousness which in earlier millenia was pictorial and mythical, has, for the most part, not been reckoned with. Psychic and spiritual facts were described. In these circumstances, outer perceptions such as the northern lights could have been stimulating or rousing, but they would be imaginatively experienced. Phenomena of colour, light and movement that could have resembled the northern lights were perceived inwardly.

It was only in the centuries prior to Plutarch that outer perception and inner vision began to separate. With this began humanity's first scientific age which was fully born in and through Aristotle (384–322 BC). Among an immense number of other things, he also observed scientifically the northern lights. Although they occur extremely seldom in the Mediterranean countries, he had most probably seen the intensive outburst of northern lights in Greece in the years 349 and 344 BC. He gives a brief description in his work,

44

Figure 4. The three following engravings were from drawings made during the French Arctic Expedition to Bossekop (now Alta) Finnmark, Norway in 1838–40. Here an arc goes over into bands.

Meterologica (1910): 'On a clear night a number of phenomena can be seen that take on the forms of chasms (*chasmata*), trenches and blood-red colours.' In line with his conception of the basic four elements, earth, water, air and fire, on which the structure of the world is founded, Aristotle describes how a vapour caused by the sun rises from the earth and collides with the sun's fire at the great altitude of the sublunar sphere where it is ignited and thus produces the coloured flashes of the northern lights. Understood in a pictorially imaginative manner, it is astonishing how exactly Aristotle discerned parts of the basic auroral process.

Figure 5. A set of pleated draperies. (French Arctic Expedition 1838–40).

In Rome Seneca (*c.* 4 BC – AD 65) described the northern lights. This writer, historian and statesman had surprisingly, a precise knowledge of auroral corona. In his work *Naturales Questiones* (1, 14, 1) he describes, among other things, this phenomenon:

> Many kinds of them are seen. There are *bothyni* [abysses]: within a surrounding corona there is a great gap in the sky like a hole dug in a circle. There are *pithiai* [casks]: an enormous round mass of fire, like a barrel, either darts by or blazes in one place. There are *chasmata* [chasms]: some area of the sky settles and, gaping in hiding — so to speak — sends out flame.

In the Mediterranean landscape the northern lights appeared

Figure 6. Curtain-like draperies fold into spirals. (French Arctic Expedition 1838–40.)

mostly on the horizon and were, therefore, coloured red by dust and clouds. These images of fire also became a characteristic symbol of the burning fall of the Roman world. Contemporary accounts, those, for instance, by Pliny the Elder (AD 23–79), are also the last precise descriptions for about a thousand years during which it was almost solely fear and superstition that governed human relationships to unusual natural phenomena. This human spiritual condition remained into the age of the Renaissance. Added to this was a mystifying belief in miracles.

In the early Middle Ages circumstances were unusual. Human beings still looked clairvoyantly into the supersensory realm of myth

47

in a dreamlike manner. The rise of the Edda in Iceland was an outcome of this clairvoyant perception; it led to the Norse history of gods and men. In narrating these myths, arising out of clairvoyant consciousness one becomes very much aware of an inability to differentiate between the external world of perception and the inner world known to imagination.

For nowhere in the Edda, despite its north European origin, can one find with certainty a description or mention of the northern lights, although many light and colour phenomena are referred to. This fact can be attributed partly to a supposedly great decrease in the activity of the northern lights during the centuries of the Elder Edda's composition (eleventh century and earlier). In the Norwegian saga, *The King's Mirror*, there is a section which up to a few years ago was regarded as quite puzzling. This work originated in the thirteenth century. In it is told how a man from Trondheim passes on to his son comprehensive knowledge and experience of the whole then known world. In connection with descriptions of Greenland, the son enquires about the northern lights. The father answers: (*King's Mirror* 1917, 149ff):

> But as to that matter which you have often inquired about,
> what those lights can be which the Greenlanders call the
> northern lights, I have no clear knowledge. I have often met
> men who have spent a long time in Greenland, but they
> do not seem to know definitely what those lights are.
> However, it is true of that subject as of many others of

Plate 3. Swinging movements in the arcs and bands are characteristic of the dynamics and course of movement of the aurora. Thus a band can suddenly disappear and another band can emerge at another place. Also parts of a band can fall away or separate parts can appear at other places in the sky. Something unexpected is always happening. The green band shown here is typical of a 'normal' appearance of the aurora.

Plate 4. The winter half of the year in the North is not as dark as is generally supposed. A main reason for this is the snow, which gives a manifold reflection of all the light from the moon and stars. Added to this is an even stronger light from the aurora, appearing every night at certain times in the farthest North. The snow reflects not only the light from the aurora, but its whole spectrum of colours. Thus the landscape acquires a vesture of colours, comparable to the colours called forth in the South by the sun.

which we have no sure knowledge, that thoughtful men will form opinions and conjectures about it and will make such guesses as seem reasonable and likely to be true. But these northern lights have this peculiar nature, that the darker the night is, the brighter they seem; and they always appear at night but never by day, — most frequently in the densest darkness and rarely by moonlight. In appearance they resemble a vast flame of fire viewed from a great distance. It also looks as if sharp points were shot from this flame up into the sky; these are of uneven height and in constant motion, now one, now another darting highest; and the light appears to blaze like a living flame. While these rays are at their highest and brightest, they give forth so much light that people out of doors can easily find their way about and can even go hunting, if need be. Where people sit in houses that have windows, it is so light inside that all within the room can see each other's faces. The light is very changeable. Sometimes it appears to grow dim, as if a black smoke or a dark fog were blown up among the rays; and then it looks very much as if the light were overcome by this smoke and about to be quenched. But as soon as the smoke begins to grow thinner, the light begins to brighten again; and it happens at times that people think they see large sparks shooting out of it as from glowing iron which has just been taken from the forge. But as night declines and day approaches, the light begins to fade; and when daylight appears, it seems to vanish entirely.

The men who have thought about and discussed these lights have guessed at three sources, one of which, it

Plate 5. At first the aurora often displays a white arc, similar to the rainbow but much larger. Movements arise and through them colours emerge, together with manifold swings and convolutions. The outcome — as in this picture — may be a waving band similar to a veil and often looking like a curtain.

Plate 6. The expansion-dynamic of the aurora is astounding. Large parts of the sky can be quickly covered with veils of colour. In rare cases the whole dome of the sky is filled with auroral colours. In this picture the electric lighting of the town of Kiruna gives an impression of the energy involved in an aurora display, far surpassing the energy produced on earth.

seems, ought to be the true one. Some hold that fire circles about the ocean and all the bodies of water that stream about on the outer sides of the globe; and since Greenland lies on the outermost edge of the earth to the north, they think it possible that these lights shine forth from the fires that encircle the outer ocean. Others have suggested that during the hours of night, when the sun's course is beneath the earth, an occasional gleam of its light may shoot up into the sky; for they insist that Greenland lies so far out on the earth's edge that the curved surface which shuts out the sunlight must be less prominent there. But there are still others who believe (and it seems to me not unlikely) that the frost and the glaciers have become so powerful there that they are able to radiate forth these flames. I know nothing further that has been conjectured on this subject, only these three theories that I have presented; as to their correctness I do not decide, though the last mentioned looks quite plausible to me.

It is evident from the son's questions and the father's answers that neither of them was acquainted with the northern lights at first hand. This is the more astonishing since it is known that at about this time an intensive sunspot activity must have given rise to a widespread aurora. This cannot, therefore, have been seen in Trondheim or its wider surroundings where, in later years, it was very often to be seen. The mystery began to resolve itself when it was recognized that the centre of the northern lights shifted slowly in relation to the North Pole. It is assumed today that in about 700 BC this centre lay somewhat north of Spitsbergen and in about 1200 lay near the New Siberian Islands. Through this displacement of the magnetic pole the whole of Norway lay a good bit south of the oval of the northern lights in 1200 and probably outside the northern lights' zone. The slow displacement of the northern lights' zone signifies a geographical extension of the already far-reaching dynamics of the aurora.

The northern lights are hardly dealt with in the great work of the Danish astronomer, Tycho Brahe (1546–1601). He left only a few obscure notes, even though he was an intensive observer of the night sky. The reason for this is that during his lifetime only very little of the northern lights was to be seen. However, in demonstrating that the comets moved on their orbits beyond the moon's sphere, he corrected a widespread fallacy which went back to the

Roman author Pliny the Elder. Pliny still regarded the comets as meteorological phenomena within the earth's atmosphere. Through Brahe's correct observation the space perceivable beyond the earth was extended and in this space the aurora's development and appearance could be seen.

On November 17, 1607 intensive northern lights developed over the whole of Europe. This was seen by Johannes Kepler (1571–1630), and accurately described by him. Galileo Galilei (1564–1642), witnessed a great outburst of the aurora in Venice in the year 1621. These two researchers give the first factual accounts of the northern lights in Central Europe. Aurora borealis, the name used internationally today, springs from Galileo. It appears for the first time in an essay that he published in 1616 together with a pupil, Guiducci. In it, in addition to comets, he deals with the northern lights and, describing the astonishing illumination in the northern sky, he concludes with the words: '. . . thus forming for us this northern dawn (*questa boreale aurora*).' In 1619 Galilei described the northern lights and offered an explanation which, in part, conforms to Aristotle:

> . . . an effect which in my opinion has no other origin than
> that a part of the vapor-laden air surrounding the earth is
> for some reason unusually rarefied and extraordinarily
> sublimated has risen above the cone of the earth's shadow
> so that its upper parts are struck by the sun and made able
> to reflect its splendor to us, thus forming for us the
> northern dawn. (Siscoe, 1978, 59, 994).

René Descartes (1596–1650), the French philosopher, wrote the work *Meteora* in which he also treats of the northern lights but his accounts do not imply that he had ever seen this phenomenon. Thus his conceptions were highly speculative. He supposed that a quantity of 'wind-clouds' would collide, put the air under pressure, and excite it, so that — similar to the then prevailing conception of the cause of lightning — light would be generated. Another of his ideas was: there is a powerful terrestrial flame that is reflected from the clouds. Another of Descartes' conceptions which kept reasserting itself over several centuries was that which saw in the aurora a reflection of sunlight on ice crystals at a great altitude. Around this time there were very few appearances of the northern lights for almost a hundred years. From about 1620 to 1725 there was a period known today as the Maunder minimum. (It is so called after the English physicist Edward W. Maunder (1851–1928). He was superintendent of the Solar Department of Greenwich Observatory and had dedicated himself particularly to this calm phase of the sun.)

The second half of the Maunder minimum coincided with the first half of the life of Edmund Halley (1656–1742), the great English astronomer after whom Halley's Comet was named. He formulated his relationship to the northern lights by saying he was dying to see the aurora and expected to die without seeing it. The following early exposition by Halley shows to what extreme constructions serious researchers of this time were led in order to explain the complex phenomenon of the aurora (1717, 427f):

> That supposing the *Earth* to be concave, with a lesser Globe included, in order to make that inner Globe capable of being inhabited, there might not improbably be contained some luminous *Medium* between the Balls, so as to make a perpetual Day below . . . And if such a *Medium* should be thus inclosed within us; what should hinder but we may be allowed to suppose that some parts of this lucid Substance may, on very rare and extraordinary Occasions, transude through and penetrate the *Cortex* of our *Earth*, and being got loose may afford the Matter whereof this our *Meteor* [aurora] consists. This seems favoured by one considerable Circumstance, *viz.* that the *Earth*, because of its diurnal Rotation, being necessarily of the Figure of a Flat *Spheroid*, the thickness of the *Cortex* in the *Polar* Parts of the Globe, is considerably less than towards the *Equator*; and therefore more likely to give Passage to these Vapours; whence a reason may be given why these lights are always seen in the North.

In 1716 Halley was blessed with the opportunity to witness the finest aurora in a century. For the Royal Society he wrote a treatise postulating a force of subtle nature. He called it *Magnetical Effluvia*, a magnetic exhalation. It is capable of penetrating all substances, including gold. Halley delineated the earth's magnetic field. The descriptions appertaining to it are linguistically somewhat aphoristic but enter with astonishingly imaginative insight into the present state of research (Halley 1717, 422–27).

> . . . which subtile Matter freely pervading the Pores of the Earth, and entering into it near its Southern Pole, may pass out again into the Ether, at the same Distance from the Northern, and with a like force; . . . this subtile Matter, no otherways discovering it self but by its Effects

on the Magnetick Needle, wholly imperceptible and at
other times invisible, may now and then, by the Concourse
of Several Causes very rarely coincident, and to us as yet
unknown, be capable of producing a small Degree of Light;
     . . . I assume the *Effluvia* of the Magnetical Matter for
this purpose, which in certain Cases may themselves
become luminous, or rather may sometimes carry with
them out of the Bowels of the Earth [to be] a sort of
Atoms proper to produce Light in the Ether.

Nevertheless, despite these far-reaching insights, Halley could not
yet discern the relationship of the aurora to the field lines of the
magnetic field surrounding the earth.

It was only a year before Halley's death, in 1741, that researchers
in Scandinavia ascertained the close connection between the magnetic
field and the northern lights. The Swedish astronomer, Anders
Celsius (1701–44) had a co-worker who was also his brother-in-law,
Olof P. Hiorter, (1696–1750). These two scientists directed their
attention to the deviation of the compass needle in the presence of
magnetic disturbances and the simultaneous appearance of the
aurora. Celsius, known for his grading of the thermometer,
published in 1733 a comprehensive treatise on the northern lights
which attracted attention throughout Europe where hitherto the
French natural philosopher, Jean de Mairan (1678–1771) had significantly expanded the conceptions concerning the aurora's origin.

Mairan brought its origin into conjunction with the zodiacal light
in the ecliptic's outer space. He assumed that the earth, in its orbit
round the sun, entered this light from time to time — at that time
it was regarded as an extension of the sun's atmosphere — and that
the aurora represented a lighting up of the zodiacal light in the
earth's extended atmosphere. Furthermore, Mairan saw a relationship
between the frequency of sun-spots and the display of the northern
lights. Thus an important step was taken, but it could not be fully
realized. Celsius did not agree with this view, yet offered no explanation of his own towards the mystery of the northern lights. His
co-worker, Hiorter, was unusually industrious. Celsius left him a
magnetic needle. Hiorter supervised this needle in Uppsala day and
night and noted his observations almost every hour. Throughout a
whole year (from 1741 to 1742) he took 6638 readings (a year has
8760 hours!).

From this, the close relationship between the aurora and movements in the magnetic field became fully evident. The full incorpor-

ation of the aurora into the magnetic field was, however, first under-taken by the Swedish physicist Johann C. Wilcke (1732–96). He became known through his publication of maps of the world inscribed with magnetic field lines and the corresponding inclinations (vertical magnetic inclinations). The sight-line into the aurora's corona lay parallel to the geomagnetic field lines. The deviating compass needle pointed in the same direction.

The progress in experimental physics in the eighteenth century proved advantageous to the Danish bishop in Trondheim, Erich Pontoppidan (1698–1764) who came to the conclusion that the aurora was an electrical phenomenon. A friend had drawn his attention to a paper by a Frenchman, M. Desaguliers, who described how heavy raindrops could be held suspended in the lighter air by electric forces. This led Pontoppidan to the idea (1751):

> One can imagine the earth's globe with its encircling air as
> a glass globe in an electrostatic machine. When the air is
> pumped out and the globe rapidly rotated then a purple
> coloured flame, which is also the colour of the aurora,
> sinks down within it; this flame must be the ignited ether
> (*aether ignens*) . . . The northern light observed in the
> direction of the pole will not only have its origin in the
> ether but will itself be ether . . .

Electrical and old ether conceptions here come into peculiar relationship. The most exact observation Pontoppidan made was that the aurora did not increase towards the north but towards in the north-west. From then on, attention began to be focussed on the magnetic pole. Halley and Mairan had already indicated a method for exact measurement of the aurora's altitude: triangulation. Two people make observations of the aurora from two different positions, far enough apart to enable them to get clear angula measurements. From the results of these measurements the height can be estimated. The difficulty with the aurora is that the observers must ascertain exactly that they are observing the same point on a stationary curtain of the aurora. This proved to be very difficult. It was the English scientist, Henry Cavendish (1731–1810) who first succeeded in using this method successfully. In 1796 he came to the astonishingly exact result of 52 to 71 miles (83 to 114 km). This method, however, could be established only through the modern media of communi-cation beginning with the twentieth century. Up to this time there reigned the greatest uncertainty with respect to the actual altitude of the aurora, for the results oscillated between ground-level and over

Figure 7. The two following illustrations show the aurora australis visible in Antarctica, portrayed during the British Antarctic Expedition of 1901–1904. The typical arc is seen here with a few bands above.

1000 kilometres (600 miles). Cavendish's results could not be verified and were not, therefore, generally recognized.

In northern Russia, the aurora was a frequent phenomenon. Exact descriptions go back to the year 919. The mysterious light played a decisive role in wars and battles. At a later date, in 1722 on the Caspian Sea near Astrachan, Peter the Great (1672–1725) saw the aurora which he described as a great fire. The extremely southern latitude of 46° N. was visited by an outburst of the aurora on the same night in Paris, Berlin and Lynn, Massachusetts (42.3°).

The great founder of Russian science, linguistics and literature, Mikhail Lomonosov (1711–65), towards the end of his life intended writing a comprehensive work on the northern lights in three parts for which his life's study seems to have predetermined him. When a boy, at his home in Kholmogory not far from the White Sea port of Archangel (64.7° N), Lomonosov often lay on the ground looking

Figure 8. Curtains of aurora australis. (British Antarctic Expedition 1901–4.)

up at the northern lights, dreaming his way into the colourful fluctuations of its forms. People often had to waken him from his trance-like state. He was the son of a poor fisherman, but through great effort and sacrifice managed to study in Moscow. In the course of time he developed into a universal scientist.

Lomonosov lived at about the same time as Benjamin Franklin (1706–90), the American writer, scientist and politician. From 1746 he occupied himself with the phenomenon of electricity and, in particular, its discharge in gas and vacuum chambers. Following up Franklin's theories, Lomonosov conducted many experiments to prove the light-emitting electrical nature of the northern lights. Connected with this was his conception of rising and sinking air streams in the region of the pole. According to his view, these generated tensions of friction which then discharged themselves in the aurora and thereby became luminous. In 1763, during the preparation of an expedition that was to discover the north-east passage to Siberia, Lomonosov spared no pains in demonstrating that there must be in the polar region a great expanse of unfrozen water from which these hypothetical warm air streams rose.

His great work on the aurora borealis was only begun; some chapters are preserved as well as the draft for: firstly, research into the origin of the aurora borealis; secondly, theory of electrical forces; thirdly, appearances (revelations) of the aurora borealis. Forty-eight drawings by Lomonosov himself were to illustrate the work. A number of these drawings are still extant and may be found in the complete edition of his works. In his book, *Rhetoric*, Lomonosov has a poem:

> But where, oh Nature, is thy law?
> From midnight lands the morning dawn emerges!
> Does not the sun take up his throne?
> Do not frozen seas ray forth his fire?
> Behold, a cold flame has enclosed us!
> Behold, in the night, came day to earth.

The end of the eighteenth century saw an incalculable profusion of theories and contradictory observations along the road to an understanding of the aurora. These were to be ordered and consolidated only in the course of the nineteenth century. In that century a science was established which possessed the possibility of eliminating speculations lacking in observation.

4. Science and the aurora

Around the beginning of the nineteenth century, scientific research began to direct its attention more and more to the aurora's magnetic and electric nature. The researcher Christopher Hansteen (1784–1873) occupied the chair for mathematics and astronomy in 1812 at the University of Christiana (Oslo) following his exposition of an award's question: 'Can all the earth's magnetic phenomena be derived from a magnetic axis, or must more be presupposed?' In 1829–30 Hansteen undertook an expedition to Siberia to investigate there the unusually strong geomagnetic field. He observed how, prior to an outburst of the aurora, the magnetic field's horizontal components increased, only to decrease after the light's display. He could also show that the highest point of an auroral arc usually lay in the neighbourhood of the observer's magnetic meridian.

The result of this research showed conclusively that the aurora was related to magnetic phenomena. Already, during his student days, Hansteen had been directed towards the significance of the earth's magnetism by the Danish physicist, Hans C. Ørsted (1777–1851). He too investigated the aurora and in 1826 referred to the fluctuating magnetic field in the neighbourhood of the aurora's arcs; these could spring from electrical discharges along the arcs. With this, Ørsted drew attention to occurrences which were not fully comprehended until some hundred years later. Only then was it discovered how the outer atmosphere, the ionosphere, is an excellent conductor of electric current and thus generates widespread occurrences of electrical events.

At this time, the question still repeatedly arose whether the aurora was not indeed somehow reflected sunlight. In order to answer this question precisely, the northern lights were observed in the years following 1800 with the aid of a polarimeter. With this apparatus, the property of light to reflect or bend (refraction) can be measured; this is called polarization. The French physicist Jean B. Biot (1774–1862), stayed on the Shetland Islands, Scotland, in 1827 in order to observe the northern lights with the aid of a polarimeter. Here he found no trace of polarization. Biot's investigation established that the aurora could not be a reflection of the sun.

During these years, the use of spectral analysis was developed; by means of an optical apparatus, the spectrometer, the coloured spectrum of a light phenomenon can be photographed. Sunlight, when photographed, shows a consistently complete colour spectrum. The colour bands and lines which arise in this way are related to certain substances in the light source; it is assumed that the spectrogram establishes the certainty of the presence of certain gases in the object photographed. As a control, these are reproduced in the laboratory and investigated spectroscopically, whereby the frequency of the photographed coloured lines are measured accurately. The Swedish physicist, Anders Jonas Ångström (1814–74) examined the aurora with a spectrometer and ascertained that it consisted of luminous gases and not, as hitherto had been thought, of other substances such as water or ice particles. The dominant colour line of the spectrogram, measured by Ångström, was yellow-green. He used a unit of measure that was later named after him; its value was one ten thousand millionth of a metre. Ångström's measurement of the yellow-green aurora gave it 5567 units of length. The exact measurement was later fixed at 5577 Å (ångström).

In the first days of September 1859 there was the greatest ever display of the aurora. In Puerto Rico (latitude 18° N) the aurora was seen even in the zenith. Had there been observers to watch it, it could probably have been seen over the whole earth. Prior to this display, an English astronomer had observed extremely bright radiating eruptions on the sun. Richard C. Carrington (1826–75) who had first studied theology, owned a private astronomical observatory in Redhill England. He was particularly dedicated to the observation of sunspots. On September 1, 1859 Carrington was drawing sunspot groupings projected by the telescope. He describes his experience (1860, 20, 13):

> . . . when within the area of the great north group . . . two patches of intensely bright and white light broke out . . .

My first impression was that by some chance a ray of light had penetrated a hole in the screen attached to the object-glass, for the brilliancy was fully equal to that of direct sunlight, but . . . I was an unprepared witness to a very different affair. I thereupon noted down the time by the chronometer, and, seeing the outburst to be very rapidly on the increase, and being somewhat flurried by the surprise, I hastily ran to call someone to witness the exhibition with me, and on returning within 60 seconds, was mortified to find that it was already much changed and enfeebled.

Eighteen hours later, the most powerful magnetic storm ever recorded swept over the earth; it caused a world-wide visible aurora. The relationship between solar flares connected with sunspots and the aurora was, for Carrington, emphatically established. However, he held back his conclusion in order to find further, more certain, confirmation.

The attention of researchers had been directed since the middle of the century towards the connection between solar activity and the aurora. Finally the Danish pedagogue and physicist, Sophus Tromholt (1852–96) established the full connection. As a teacher he got a transfer from Denmark to Norway and soon received two state stipends which made it possible for him to devote all his energy to auroral research. Tromholt stayed for twenty-five years in Norway and during this time he installed a widely distributed network of observatories from which he received findings from more than a hundred Scandinavian localities. Apart from this, several thousand individuals contributed to the completion of the observations.

During the first International Polar Year (1882/3) he was responsible for one of the two Norwegian observatories in Lapland

Plate 7. An unlimited wealth of colours is characteristic of the aurora. If in addition the aurora is below the horizon — as in this picture — one can witness shades of colour called forth through denser layers of air or light clouds.

Plate 8. The aurora has a milky white appearance not only as an initial arc but also as independent arcs and bands which inscribe their flowing signs in the sky. If behind clouds, the aurora seems to be a meteorological appearance. The landscape is then so brightly lit, that everything is clearly visible.

4. SCIENCE AND THE AURORA

(Kautokeino). Here in the north, Tromholt began to interest himself intensively in the life of the Lapps; photographs show him in Lapp costume together with his observatory equipment. His experiences during this sojourn in the far north are described in his book. This work, translated into many languages, deals, above all, with the culture of the Lapps; the chapter on the aurora is professional and fundamental, but was largely overlooked by auroral research because the book did not appear as a scientific publication. On the basis of the many observations received and his own experiences, Tromholt had formed an exact picture of the auroral oval. He was able to arrange the phenomenon correctly in its planetary dimensions, not recognized for the most part, by other researchers, and described the oval (1885, 1, 216):

> On account of the great circumference of the earth, in proportion to the height of the aurora, only a small portion of such a ring would be visible at one time, and each observer only see his own portion, the situation of which in relation to *his* horizon and the Zenith will depend on *his* position in relation to the auroral ring.

This ring — the oval — pulsates, spreads out dynamically in an equatorial direction, while its low light centre also expands and contracts again in conformity with the activity of the sun, the sunspot rhythm. Added to this is the continually changing relationship between the oval and the rotating earth below it.

It was the achievement of Tromholt to have grasped broadly this relationship phenomenologically. Thus the aurora was recognized as a planetary-cosmic formation — something that, until this time, had remained unknown and undiscovered. About a hundred years later, the auroral oval could be photographed from beyond the earth's circumference (see Plate 11).

Plate 9. The aurora often seems to be pressing vertically right down to the earth. Then it can resemble tongues of flame. The snow on the tree in this picture has a pink reflection of a red aurora not visible in the picture.

Plate 10. The aurora can give an effect of radiant revelations from the heights, thus evoking the mood of Christmas. But the coloured 'rays' are broad bands, falling vertically in folds. Seen from a spacecraft they give an impression of coloured columns of light. In the next moment this radiant appearance may disappear back into darkness.

With this discovery in about 1879, began a scientific development which led to the present-day conception of the aurora. At its instigation stood a quantitative view of the auroral phenomenon.

In Europe, the northern lights are more often visible from latitude 60° (Oslo-Helsinki-Leningrad). This latitude forms a kind of light-dark frontier. At this latitude the 'white nights' begin and in summer it remains light almost throughout the night. Several hundred miles to the north, this frontier is clearly crossed; here, at

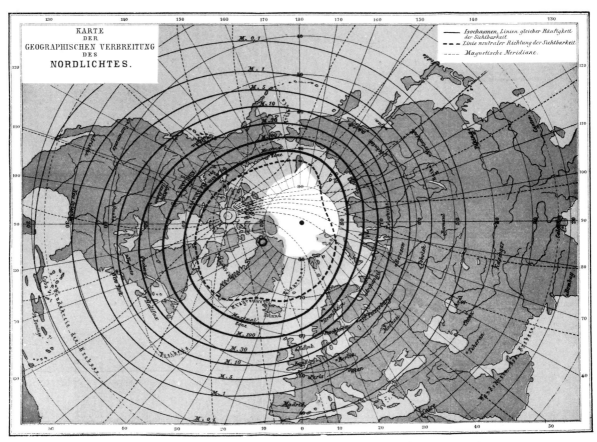

Figure 9. A map drawn by Hermann Fritz in 1881, with isometric lines, called isochasms, marking the places where the aurora is seen with equal frequency. The centre of this aurora zone is near the geomagnetic North Pole of the earth in North-West Greenland, (circle), 800 km (500 miles) north-east of the magnetic North Pole (double circle).

the height of summer the light drives out all the night's darkness. In this zone the northern lights appear frequently in the dark season of the year, and are clearly visible. Here, immediately north of latitude 60°, both light frontiers coincide: in the autumn the waning sunlight is superseded by the occasionally developing northern lights. Further north, extending to Spitsbergen (80°), the aurora becomes more frequent, more intensive and rich in formations. In the furthermost north, beyond latitude 80°, the situation changes.

The German physicist Herman Fritz (1830–93) published in 1881 the first precise accounts on the frequency of the aurora in the Northern hemisphere. On a map of the world, centered on the North Pole, he drew lines through equivalent auroral frequencies (see Figure 9). These lines are called isochasms, from the Greek word *chasmata*, a term already used by Aristotle for an appearance of the northern lights. A fundamental preparatory work for Fritz's isochasmic map was the auroral zone map produced by Professor Elias Loomis (1811–89) at Yale in 1860.

The isochasms show the aurora visible on earth as a huge oval embracing, in its entirety, the geographical and magnetic North Poles. This oval, delineated by the isochasms on the earth's surface, is called the auroral zone. Somewhat in the centre of this zone is the geomagnetic pole, which is, therefore, also the auroral pole. The smaller, actual auroral oval floating in the altitudes above it is forced away by the sun's light-streams to the sunless side of the earth. Thereby, the oval-centre appears — in relationship to the daily rotating earth below it — continually displaced also in its position relative to the geomagnetic pole (see Figure 12).

This is equally so in the Antarctic. Thus the earth's auroral ovals as a whole swing with the rotation of the geomagnetic poles round the geographical poles, being constantly orientated away from the sun.

The geomagnetic North Pole is currently situated in North-West Greenland at Thule (about 79° N, 70° W); it is the centre of the earth's radial magnetism, the magnetic field around the earth. In passing over to terrestrial magnetism, this pole is displaced by irregularities within the earth's crust. So the magnetic pole (compass north) is near Bathurst Island in northern Canada, 800 km (500 miles) south-west of the geomagnetic pole, the centre of the magnetic fields in, and tied to, the earth. About 1200 km (750 miles) north of the geomagnetic pole lies the earth's geographical North Pole.

The isochasm of the most frequent appearance of the aurora is an oval band on the earth, with a breadth of 500 km (300 miles), about 2000 km (1250 miles), distant from the geomagnetic pole (aurora's centre). Within the area enclosing the auroral oval — somewhat above latitude 80° in Europe — the visible aurora decreases. In the region around the pole itself the aurora is hardly visible. While the aurora's activity within the oval band develops horizontally, this direction changes to the vertical in the polar regions, where the altitude of the aurora increases and the light itself becomes weaker and invisible.

In 1881, Sophus Tromholt summed up his observations in a paper. He had noticed that in the auroral zone in northern Norway there was a regular recurrence of displays, and that, for example, the further north he went, the later in the night hours the auroral maximum occurred. He could also build on the directives of earlier Scandinavian researchers. The Danish justice minister Erich J. Jessen-Schardeboll (1705–83) had already drawn attention to the global dimension of the oval's form, and the Norwegian Christopher Hansteen (1784–1873) saw the aurora's oval as incorporated in the surrounding field lines of the geomagnetic north pole. Tromholt, however, was the first to observe, about 1879, how the auroral oval spread towards the equator with an increase in solar activity during the eleven-year sunspot cycles. Tromholt's far-reaching discoveries were not accepted, and his enthusiastic and large-scale work was, until recently, overlooked and unacknowledged.

It is only in the present day that his towering significance in the field of auroral research is acknowledged. Even in the mid-eighties of the last century Tromholt wrote the humble and enthusiastic words (1885, 1, 287):

Will man ever decipher the characters which the Aurora
Borealis draws in fire on the dark sky? Will his eye ever
penetrate the mysteries of Creation which hidden behind
this dazzling drapery of colour and light? Who will
venture to answer! Only the Future knows the reply.

The zone of maximum frequency runs as an isochasm through northern Norway (Tromsø), northern Canada (Hudson Bay), northern Alaska and the surfaces of the sea and ice north of the Russian continent. In this zone, the northern lights are visible almost every night. In connection with the earth's daily rotation there arises a continually changing relationship of the oval to the isochasms' geographical locality. Ever new sections of the oval come to stand above the locality of observation. On this account the intensity and character of the aurora is continually changing. For, within the oval band, it has very different, though essentially defined forms of display. Thus in far-northern regions, as for example, Spitsbergen where the sun does not rise in winter time, the so-called daytime aurora is visible as a finely divided, weak red-shining phenomenon. This daytime aurora is the aurora which is visible about midday during the winter polar-day darkness. In contrast to this, the northern lights of evening and night form the aurora's proper and distinct display. However, even this can be seen, morning or afternoon during the day as long as it is dark enough.

In regions lying further south, the frequency of the auroral phenomenon decreases rapidly. On the isochasm which in Scandinavia goes through latitude 60° lie Oslo, Aberdeen in Scotland, Donegal in Ireland, Newfoundland, Quebec and Lake Superior in Canada, Anchorage in Alaska, Siberia and Archangel in Russia. Within this belt, the aurora appears during thirty to forty nights in the year and is clearly visible if not very frequently because greater cloud formation or haze hinders visibility on many nights.

In Central Europe (Southern United States) the frequency sinks to about one to seven nights in the year; the aurora is thus seldom visible; however, with careful observation it can certainly be seen. In the Mediterranean region, in Mexico, in Hokkaido, Japan and in the regions of the Caspian and Black Seas, the aurora appears only about once every ten years and is practically no longer visible. Nevertheless, very seldom, powerful auroral displays can be seen over the whole earth.

The close relationship of the aurora and magnetism is evident in the approximately centring of the auroral oval in the geomagnetic pole. The aurora appears along the lines of magnetic force, the bearers of magnetism in the earth's circumference in the polar regions. These lines of magnetic force encircle the earth like a longitudinally structured network. The lines of magnetic force dip towards the poles and penetrate the earth in the polar regions (Figure 10). An observer in the polar region would see these lines — were they visible — as powerful, high-rising cliffs around him on all sides. On the other hand, an observer in lower latitudes would see lines sloping away towards the pole. This magnetic force line structure of the adjacent earth's circumference is not rigid, but is in a sensitive labile state that can quickly pass into vibrations, eruptions, and wholly unexpected powerful movements (magnetic field

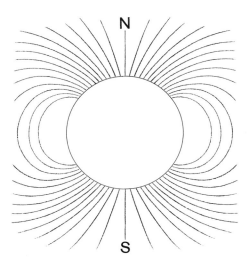

Figure 10. The magnetic field around a magnetized sphere, or the earth.

variations). The condition is comparable to that of the earth's atmosphere. As here, so too in this magnetic field, agitation may give rise to magnetic storms. The aurora and, together with it the auroral oval, rises on the structure of this magnetism encircling the earth. This structure, as will be more precisely described (see p. 71ff), is influenced by the magnetism of the stream of particles arriving from the sun, the solar wind.

It is a characteristic of the auroral display that it has hitherto remained, for the most part, concealed from human perception. For in the regions of its visibility in the northern hemisphere there is, on average, only one inhabitant per two square kilometres (about one square mile). In the southern hemisphere, the aurora australis becomes visible in regions that are virtually devoid of human beings. In Melbourne, Australia, its appearance is about as frequent as in Central Europe. Thus only a diminutive fraction of humanity lives in the immediate vicinity of the aurora's zone of visibility. It is, therefore, exceptional to ordinary human experience.

It is only with the arrival of the achievements of science and technology in the nineteenth and twentieth centuries — extra-terrestrial observations by satellite — that a general awareness of the aurora has today been made possible. Moreover, a comprehensive global phenomenology is now possible for the first time. This has demonstrated decisively that the auroral displays within the ovals north and south of the earth are approximately similar in their development and are hence related. This confirms a conjecture made in 1872 by Norway's founder of meteorology, Henrik Mohn (1835–1916).

The physical dynamics of this cosmic phenomenon encompassing the earth was indeed extraordinarily difficult to understand. The Swede Karl S. Lemström (1838–1904) turned the whole question upside down. According to him, the aurora arose because of an electric current streaming upwards out of the earth. The colourful discharge phenomena would be formed only in airless space. In order to prove this, he took a mesh of several hundred square metres of spiked coiled copper wire to the summit of a mountain near Sodänkylä (Orantunturi) in Finland, earthed it to a sunken platinum plate, and ran an electric current through the whole arrangement. As a result, Lemström described a dull yellowish radiating light that contained faint spectroscopic traces of auroral light. Tromholt and other researchers repeated these experiments in other contexts, without being able to confirm Lemström's results.

The Danish researcher and director of the meteorological institute, Adam Paulsen (1833–1907) took over Tromholt's results and continued work on them. The exact physical nature of the surface eruptions on the sun was still unknown. Paulsen assumed that these flares gave rise to ultraviolet radiation which, in turn, caused the aurora, and in this respect he identified it with the cathode rays already discovered — the stream of electric current in vacuum tubes. Paulsen wrote a decisive statement (1896) revealing how the outlook of auroral research is now clearly directed towards physically understood cosmic phenomena: 'I think I can demonstrate that the conception of the aurora as a phenomenon formed by the absorption of cathode rays will explain the aurora, its relationship to the earth's magnetism and the varying periods of intensity in its appearance.' This conception, though incomplete, was for the present correct in essentials and was carried over into the following century. Attention was thereby drawn to the cosmic stream of ions coming from the sun which, in the second half of the twentieth century could be extensively observed.

The scientific work of the Norwegian auroral researcher Kristian Birkeland (1867–1917) made a big step forward. He had worked and studied in Bonn, Geneva and Leipzig. In 1898 he became a professor in Oslo and was an inspiring teacher at Christiania University. Two years earlier, he had presented his auroral theory: that electrically charged particles from the sun reach the terrestrial magnetic field at almost the speed of light. They are caught up here and conducted along the magnetic lines of force to the poles. In doing so, the particles run through complex spiral paths and upon their meeting with the earth's atmospheric gases they are retarded and become luminous.

Birkeland soon went ahead to test this theory by thorough experiment. He constructed a model: in a vacuum chamber of about 1.5 cubic metres (50 cubic ft) capacity there was hung a sphere that contained a charged electromagnet. The sphere was a model of the earth with its magnetic field, the surrounding vacuum represented the empty space in the universe. The 'terrestrial globe' 'Terrella' was bombarded by clouds of electron particles, and luminous rings were formed around both poles of the magnetized sphere. Birkeland had produced an artificial aurora. His model, and the experiment made about 1910, resembled the principle of television.

Birkeland now went ahead with calculating the path of the injected particles. This, despite immense labour was, to begin with, an insoluble problem. Like Tromholt, Birkeland set up aurora stations far across the Scandinavian peninsula: in northern Norway (Bossekop), Iceland, Spitsbergen and Novaya Zemlya. His observations, calculations and, above all, his imaginative conjectures led him to the view that the same particles that give rise to the aurora are also the cause of the deviations in the geomagnetic field. Birkeland described and calculated the electric forces in the outer atmosphere (ionosphere) and portrayed how, to begin with, these followed the geomagnetic lines of force and then, with decreasing altitude, were transferred to the auroral arcs. These energy storms are still called Birkeland currents. The basic difficulty in Birkeland's interpretation arose because the physical nature of the oncoming solar particles was unknown; they were considered to be of the nature of light, but here an unsolved discrepancy arose between the particles moving at the speed of light and the clear observation that, following a solar eruption, at least half a day passed before the aurora lit up.

Through Birkeland's multiple efforts, geophysics was founded and attracted enthusiastic students. The best-known was Carl Størmer (1874–1957). In 1904 he was already among the circle of scientists inspired by Birkeland. Størmer was a mathematician; he took over from Birkeland the calculating of particle trajectories. Together with his assistants, Størmer undertook about 18 000 hours of calculations. In 1907 he was able to publish an account of his findings which was not fully acknowledged until fifty years later in the International Geophysical Year of 1957. Here he put forward his calculations of the paths of charged particles that move within the earth's dipolar field. Størmer showed how the incoming particles approach the polar regions in ever closer spirals until momentarily they come to a stop close to the earth where they 'reflect' for a shorter or longer time. Afterwards, the particles could immediately transfer to the other terrestrial pole where the same occurrence is repeated. The particles swing back and forth in their 'captivity' in a time-span of about one second. Thus Størmer had described an occurrence that was discovered only fifty years later in the highly charged Van Allen radiation belt. Here, then, was the reason for the simultaneous appearance of the aurora at both the North and South Pole.

Størmer's research was directed exclusively towards a quantitative material understanding of the auroral phenomenon whereby he was aided by the rise of photography in ascertaining the exact height and material substance of the auroral display. Concerning this he wrote (Brekke, Egeland 1979, 72):

> The only certain and objective method is photography. However, all attempts to photograph the northern lights were, for a long time, in vain. It was only in 1892 that two German researchers travelling to Bossekop succeeded in taking a photograph of a brightly lit curtain with an exposure of only seven seconds. This, however, was the only picture ever taken with a short exposure until I made systematic experiments in auroral photography in 1909. Through experiment, I found a small very fast photographic lens which gave excellent results. With this and a plate sensitive to violet I succeeded in taking pictures of strong northern lights with an exposure time of one second and less.
>
> After the problem of photographing the aurora was satisfactorily solved, I made expeditions to Bossekop in 1910 and 1913 to photograph the aurora and determine its altitude by photographing it simultaneously from two stations at an equal distance in opposite directions, connected by telephone. The stars also appear on the plates and by observing the different positions of the aurora against the background of the stars as seen from each station the altitude can be calculated by gauging the dimensions on the plates.

69

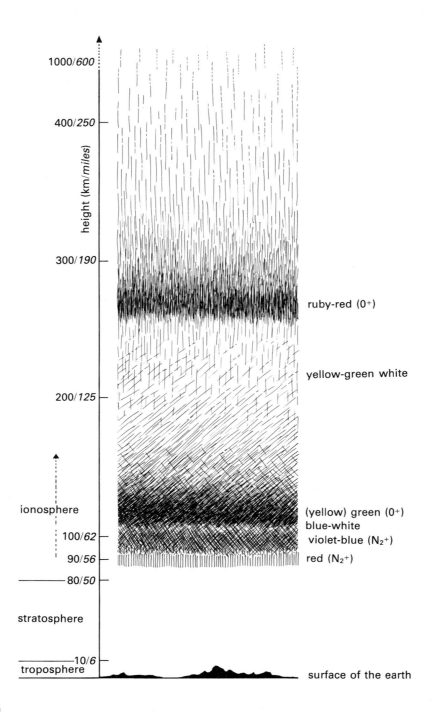

height (km/*miles*)

1000/*600*

400/*250*

300/*190*

ruby-red (0+)

yellow-green white

200/*125*

ionosphere

(yellow) green (0+)
blue-white
100/*62*

violet-blue (N₂+)
90/*56*

red (N₂+)

80/*50*

stratosphere

10/*6*

troposphere

surface of the earth

4. SCIENCE AND THE AURORA

Størmer took 40 000 photographs of the aurora of which 9 000 were taken simultaneously from two positions. He was, therefore, the researcher who ascertained the aurora's altitude with unambiguous exactitude. It begins at somewhat over 70 km (45 miles) reaches an altitude of 105 km (65 miles) where the aurora is mostly to be seen, and, in ever-diminishing quantity, stretches upwards to about 900 km (550 miles). Apart from this, Størmer discovered the aurora illuminated by the sun at an altitude above some 200 km (125 miles). This is very faintly visible in the late twilight hours.

Another researcher who belonged to K. Birkeland's circle was Lars Vegard (1880–1963). From 1905 he was for several years Birkeland's assistant. Vegard devoted himself to the aurora's spectral analysis. In this he continued the work of Ångström, who had discovered the aurora's green lines, which now constituted a problem, for nowhere could a gas be found that showed the same wavelength in spectral analysis. It was only many years later (1923) that these lines were identified by showing that they were based on an emission that is possible only in very rarefied media, as in the upper atmosphere.

The aurora's light and colour are conceived as the result of an encounter between solar related plasmic particles and gas particles in the earth's upper atmosphere. The material structure of atmospheric layers in the aurora was established by comparing the results of spectroscopic investigations in the aurora with the spectroscopic characteristics of gases known in the physical terrestrial realm. It was ascertained that at the altitude of the aurora, atomic and molecular oxygen and nitrogen are predominant. Their presence stretches over many hundreds of kilometres. The lighting-up at different altitudes is occasioned by the fluctuating intensity (velocity) of the oncoming particles. Thus particles with the greatest velocity penetrate most deeply into the atmosphere. It has been shown that in the lowest regions of the aurora, below a hundred kilometres, (60 miles) the blue-violet and red bands of the nitrogen spectrum predominate; between 100 and 240 km (60 – 150 miles) the green oxygen line is strongest, and above an altitude of 240 km (150 miles) red oxygen lines appear. A relationship between the aurora's

Figure 11. Distribution of the aurora in terms of height, showing its colours and the element present. The white colour arises as a mixture of the complementary colours of the aurora.

71

colours and particular terrestrial substances was thus established (see Figure 11).

A connection with solar-related substances was likewise sought for. As it had long been known that helium and hydrogen emanated from the sun in ionized processes, one expected to find these in the auroral spectrum, but they were not discovered for a long time. It was only in 1939 that Vegard discovered the hydrogen line in the spectrometer. He started with the hypothesis that, if it were negatively charged solar electrons that cause the aurora, they must be accompanied by positively charged nuclei, called protons or ions. Without the latter the negative electrons would on their way enter into a polarized field to the sun and thus be diverted.

The English physicist Sir Arthur Schuster (1851–1934) had already drawn attention to this problem. In 1952 Vegard wrote (Brekke, Egeland 1979, 75):

> In the years 1939–41 I had already succeeded in arriving at a direct proof that these ray-bundles were built up as I had presupposed [electrons and ions]. In Oslo in 1939 we took one series of auroral spectrograms in which the hydrogen spectrum [line] appeared particularly strong. This showed that at specific times the sun emitted positive ions [protons].
>
> In the following years we were able to record several spectrograms with strong hydrogen lines. In the winter of

Plate 11. A picture of ultra-violet light taken from a satellite at a height of 20 300 km (12 700 miles) on November 8, 1981. The auroral oval is clearly visible against the continents, superimposed by computer. The centre of the plotted latitudes is not the geographic North Pole but the geomagnetic North Pole near Thule in North-West Greenland which is also the centre of the auroral oval. The oval remains opposite the direction of the sun. At the time of this photograph, Asia was in sunlight while the broadest layer of the oval was over Labrador. The Northwest Territories are entering into the auroral oval in the evening while Scandinavia (top right) is emerging from the oval at dawn.

Plates 12 & 13. Photographs in the evening at intervals of 30 seconds with constant aperture and exposure. They show the building up and reconstruction of auroral formations in the course of time (January 28, 1982, at Kiruna, Sweden, 67.8 ° N, looking north-east.)

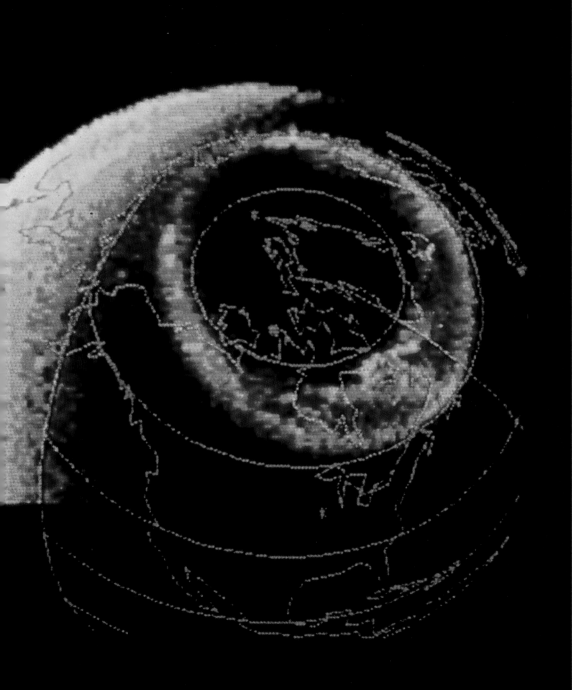

1939–40 at the auroral observatory in Tromsø we were able
to record a series of strongly exposed spectrograms with
a spectrograph which had a significantly greater resolution
than that used in Oslo. With the aid of these records we
could, for once, ascertain with absolute certainty that we
were dealing with hydrogen lines; moreover, on some of
these spectrograms the hydrogen lines took on the form of
narrow bands which were very much shifted towards the
shorter wavelengths . . . This spread and shift in the
direction of the shorter wavelengths could not be
attributed to an unsharp image, because the other lines
closer in were very well focused. It could be caused only
by the fact that the hydrogen atoms streaming from the
light were in fast movement and above all in the direction
of the observer, that is down to the earth.

This discovery by Vegard was a breakthrough in auroral
research. The so-called proton aurora had been discovered. Observation of the higher wave frequency — the short waves — of
hydrogen protons could be interpreted as a result of the Doppler
effect. The colour of the proton's light is red and the faster the
hydrogen carriers move towards the earth the more they shift
towards the violet end of the spectrum.

Attempts have also been made to determine the temperature in
the auroral display. It is assumed that at altitudes of 100 to 150 km
(60 to 95 miles) the average temperature vacillates between $-70°$ and
$+427°C$ ($-100°$ to $800°F$).

In the meantime, prior to the International Geophysical Year of
1957–8, it was known that the cause that triggered off the auroral
display was a negatively as well as a positively charged stream of
particles. The human spirit of research had intuitively sensed the
extra-terrestrial physical reality of the sun's activity without having
directly experienced its corresponding stream, because it lies in the
extra-terrestrial realm of human perception.

In October 1957 the Russian satellite *Sputnik I* was put in orbit

*Plate 14. The red colour in the aurora has usually only a limited spread;
it seldom covers a wide expanse. In this photograph (taken at 10 pm in the
Esrange Mountains in Northern Sweden) the red streaming right down to
the horizon is thus exceptional. It was accompanied by unusually strong
solar activity, confirming the connection between the two phenomena.*

round the earth. The space age had become a reality. This event accelerated the American effort in that direction. In January 1958 they started the satellite *Explorer I* which carried a geiger counter that had been developed by a research group led by James Van Allen. Following the evaluation of the counter's results in May 1958, it was shown to have been blocked. The powerful radiation (X-rays among others) had penetrated the counter in such quantity that it

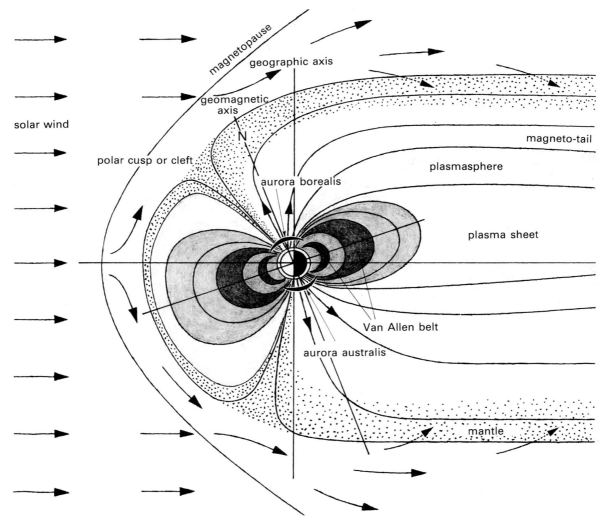

Figure 12. The magnetic structure around the earth.

could not register any more. With regard to the projected space trip, the surprisingly intensive radiation in certain regions of extra-terrestrial space created a shock; human penetration into certain zones of space in the vicinity of the earth became questionable. This arose from the discovery of several heavily energy-charged belts around the earth's equator named the Van Allen belt, after their discoverer. By means of further satellite probes and rocket flights the indirect and immediate effects of space travel on human beings were established.

This expansion was a turning point for auroral research; it became fully global and international. A completely unknown region of the earth was discovered and researched. The form and limit of the earth's magnetic field, hitherto arrived at theoretically by calculation and hypothesis, could now be measured. The magnetosphere as a protecting shield and bearer of physical-energy processes was now discovered. The image of the world had grown larger; it was no longer an isolated body surrounded by empty, cold nothingness. The earth is embedded and enshrouded in sunlike occurrences that are describable, measurable and attainable. In connection with this event the auroral researcher Robert H. Eather wrote (1980, 217):

> Modern understanding of the aurora is tied up with our understanding of the magnetosphere as a whole. Even the word *magnetosphere* is relatively new in science having been coined by Gold in 1958 to describe the region of near-earth space that is threaded by magnetic field lines linked to the earth and in which very hot or ionized gas dominates over the neutral atmosphere. It thus represents the outer limits of man's environment and is populated with ions and electrons originating in both the earth's atmosphere and the sun's atmosphere. It has become clear in recent years that the magnetosphere must be studied as a whole, as one single system of strongly interacting regions, none of which can be considered in isolation. Thus theoretical descriptions are almost prohibitively complicated, and a given observational manifestation such as the aurora is part of a complicated closed chain of cause and effect relationships.

The discovery of the magnetosphere led, at the same time, to the discovery of the solar plasma, also called solar wind. Both were theoretically known decades before, but the knowledge was incomplete. Already in 1931 the English physicists Sydney Chapman

(1888–1970) and V. C. A. Ferraro (1907–74) had presupposed the existence of a solar wind whose current would cause a cavity in the earth's surrounding magnetic field. However, the nature of such a solar wind was unknown. In the middle of the century the German physicist Ludwig Biermann had been able to make calculations which showed that the tails of comets, which always trail away from the sun, are not impelled in this direction by sunlight radiation but that another influence from the sun must be present. Surprisingly, the Norwegian K. Birkeland had expounded this view already in 1908, but it had been pushed aside by the hypothesis that light radiation exerted pressure.

In 1959, exactly a hundred years after the worldwide auroral display in 1859, the solar wind was discovered by satellites. The solar wind was shown to be a stream of particles that had nothing to do with the many known types of solar radiation, which are all related to light, from the ultraviolet rays through the daylight colours to infra-red rays. All these rays are related by travelling at the speed of light, about 300 000 km per second (196 000 miles/s). The solar wind, on the contrary, has the nature of a plasmic substance. Its particles can be measured and counted despite their incredible minuteness and extremely rarefied dispersion through space. In relation to their scarcity, their behaviour is extremely energetic. It has been shown, however, that a comparison of the solar plasma's velocity in space with terrestrial wind is not entirely unjustifiable. The solar wind moves at about 200 to 1500 km per second (120 to 950 miles/s). In cosmic terms, measured against light, this is very slow, about three hundred times slower than the speed of light. Hence the human mind is well able to form conceptions of this velocity in space. This velocity also suggests the transportation of substance, and, apart from this, the variation in speed is related to wind.

The solar plasma fills the whole of interplanetary space as far as the trans-Saturn planets. There, it meets the cosmic radiation of outer space which is dangerous to life, holds it back and forms an envelope round our planetary system. The solar plasma consists essentially of ionized hydrogen and helium. These very attenuated elements speed through space as electrons and protons and carry the sun's magnetic energy and lines of magnetic force. The electrons are negatively, the protons (and ions) positively, charged; the whole stream is equally charged. A scheme emerges that was already outlined by the Norwegian spectroscopist, Lars Vegard in 1939.

4. SCIENCE AND THE AURORA

The magnetosphere's structure has been researched with innumerable measurements around the earth for fifteen years. This magnetosphere is a hollow sheath full of energy systems surrounding the earth. But for external influences it would be identical with the earth's lines of magnetic field, with polar cusps or clefts centred at the North and South Poles. However, the perpetually flowing solar wind changes the form of the unstable magnetosphere. On the sun's side this sphere is pressed far down to about 60 000 km (37 500 miles), or about five earth-diameters, above the earth. On this boundary there is formed an entry layer (with turbulence). For the most part, the solar wind flows over this region. In the currents flowing along the magnetopause solar and terrestrial magnetic lines merge into one another. The earth's magnetosphere is drawn along in the solar wind-stream, the theoretical spherical form is stretches away from the sun and formed into a hollow tail that stretches several hundred thousand kilometres far out into space to the orbit of the moon. This streaming past of the solar wind generates powerful electromagnetic forces.

The Swedish physicist Hannes Alfvén, who received the Nobel prize in 1970 for his work in this field, brought the charge at the

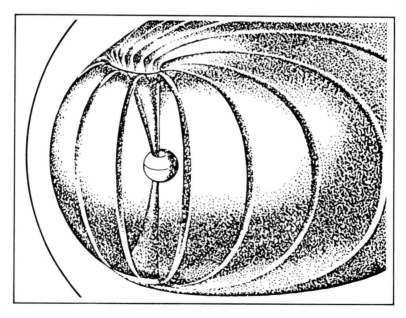

Figure 13. Magnetic field showing the polar cusp or cleft.

boundary of the magnetosphere, the magnetopause, into relationship with the aurora's formation. For decades, even before the exact identification of the magnetosphere, it was supposed that the ionized solar particles enter the magnetosphere with the solar wind in a roundabout, indirect spiralling way and then produce the aurora on the terrestrial poles. Such an entry, however, has never been established. The small region round the magnetic poles is indeed not magnetically isolated. The field-lines that penetrate or radiate from here create chasm-like cusp openings on the sun side of the magnetosphere. The solar plasma to some extent can enter directly through these funnel-shaped openings.

This phenomenon was perceived clairvoyantly in earlier times. In the Norwegian *King's Mirror* of the thirteenth century there is a graphically exact description of this event. In this narrative, the earth's surrounding atmosphere is still called the 'great or empty sea streaming round the world', similar to the biblical Genesis speaking of the waters 'above the firmament' (Gen.1:7) to designate the substance beyond the firmament. The Norwegian document says (1917, 148):

> It has been stated as a fact that Greenland lies on the outermost edge of the earth toward the north; and I do not believe there is any land in the home-circle beyond Greenland, only the great ocean that runs around the earth. And we are told by men who are informed that alongside Greenland the channel is cut through which the wide ocean [here the author of the *King's Mirror* takes up the conception of the sea surrounding the earth's circumference; it is called the 'empty' sea in contrast to the sea that contains the inhabited mainland and islands] rushes into the gap that lies between the land masses and finally branches out into fjords and inlets which cut in between the lands wherever the sea is allowed to flow out upon the earth's surface.

The incised sound and the gaps are imaginatively perceived images for the funnel-like opening through which the plasma coming from afar (the 'empty' sea) enters the terrestrial sphere; in our present-day language: the earth round which the magnetosphere streams. The imaginative perceptions of this old mode of knowing sees the terrestrial, horizontal planes of furthest space together with the heavenly heights; space on and above the earth is seen together;

this perception overflows mostly into the second dimension and describes, above all, dynamic events.

The Greek stream flowing right round the earth (the *Okeanos*) is, like the 'empty' sea, a corresponding image, and arises out of the same consciousness. The reason why the narrator of the *King's Mirror* receives his knowledge from Greenland is to be sought in the fact that the geomagnetic pole is shifting. In AD 1200 it lay, relative to its present position, on the opposite side of the North Pole near the New Siberian Islands. Because of this, the auroral oval was displaced so that at this time Norway lay outside the auroral zone while Northern Greenland still lay fully within it.

The stream of solar particles now penetrates into the regions of the open lines of magnetic force above the geomagnetic pole directly into the terrestrial environment. In so doing, it fuses with the funnel-shaped converging lines of force which act as a powerful brake on it. This gives rise to a barely perceptible, high aurora which fits into the vault of the heavens like a delicate pink cupola in the far north, around Spitsbergen, even during the dark polar 'day' in winter.

This dayside aurora was first observed and measured in 1960. It is occasionally visible to the naked eye. In this aurora, the solar particles have only the original velocity with which they left the sun and this is not sufficient to produce the well-known intensively luminous aurora.

Within the magnetosphere, powerful electromagnetic circulatory systems are formed. The parts closest to the earth rotate with it. This is the plasmasphere, around which the outer systems are formed together with the boundary layer of the magnetopause; these are quiescently orientated towards the sun.

Within the entire magnetosphere there is also plasma which could justifiably be called solar-terrestrial plasma; in contrast to the solar plasma it can have peculiar characteristics. It is concentrated in the plasmasphere and also in the Van Allen belts. The greatest concentration however, is to be found in a nucleus of the long magneto-tail. The central region is named the plasma sheet, towards which most attention is today directed.

When, with particular intensity, the solar plasma from outside sets the magnetosphere vibrating through pressure and friction and thereby energizes it, then the magnetosphere's nucleus (plasma sheet) is enriched, is put under tension and discharged. This discharge pushes the plasma in the direction of the earth's surroundings and, at the same time, in the opposite direction: out into space through the open side of the magnetosphere turned away from the sun. It is only through this happening that the terrestrial-solar plasma receives the energy and thereby velocity by means of which it is driven from the sunless side on to the magnetic lines of force to the terrestrial poles and appears in the evening and night sky as the aurora.

Closer to the earth there arise subordinate magnetic storms through the superimposed magnetosphere discharge, which appear as stormlike plasma eruptions. The sectors of these subordinate magnetic storms are visible as unusual auroral displays within the auroral oval. These local auroral movements have received the name substorms. With regard to the origin of the magnetosphere discharges, plasma researchers at present speak of an occurrence which is equivalent to a primordial solar activity in this extended terrestrial space (Evans 1982, 472f).

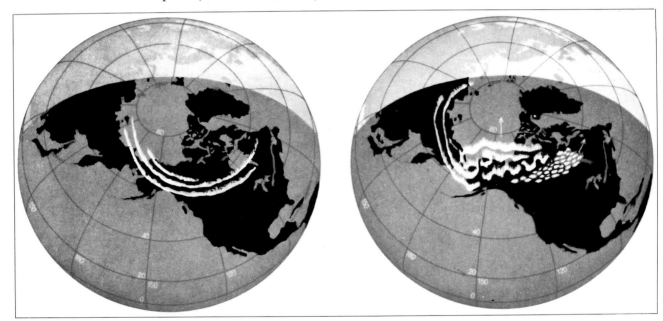

Figure 14. A composite sketch based on many photographs showing a magnetic substorm as it would be seen at a great distance from the earth. On the left, there are quiet auroral arcs within the oval. On the right a substorm is arising; the arcs fold and begin to dissolve, in order to distribute themselves more widely (from Akasofu 1976).

As a result, magnetic flux accumulates on the nightside until
some form of instability triggers its release. In this process,
some of the magnetic energy is converted to the energy of
the plasma sheet particles in what may be the terrestrial
analog of a solar flare.

The velocity of the magnetosphere plasma is several times that of
the plasma coming from the sun.

The enigma is: Where does this nucleus plasma so rich in energy
within the magnetosphere come from? It could once have originated
in the sun, penetrated into the pole's cusp to be then, through circulation, led to the plasma layer on the inside of the magnetosphere in
the so-called mantle. Or the same plasma penetrates the boundary
(magnetopause) by the interplanetary (solar) magnetic field lines
merging with the geomagnetic field lines thus allowing the solar
plasma to enter directly into the magnetosphere. However, the latest
research investigations show that the solar wind alone is not the only
cause of the energetic plasma within the magnetosphere. Georg
Gustafsson writes in this connection (1982, 38, 9): 'There are,
indeed, energy-laden helium and oxygen ions also in the outer
magnetosphere shown to be of ionosphere origin, from which one
can deduce that the solar wind is not the only source of hot plasma
in the magnetosphere.'

The same facts are confirmed by Robert H. Eather (1980, 221):
'A third possible source of plasma sheet particles may be the loss of
the earth's own ionospheric particles along the open magnetic field
lines from the polar cap regions.' This third possibility suggests that
one could call the plasma of the magnetosphere's nucleus (the plasma
sheet) terrestrial plasma or terrestrial-solar plasma, as this plasma
bears essential characteristics of the solar plasma. Many auroral
researchers leave this an open question. Many, however, bring this
as yet unknown field of incoming energy and the cause of its
concentration much closer to the earth and see it as great electric
fields in the immediate vicinity of the earth's environment.

The discoveries of the most recent auroral research have led to
the view that the cause of the aurora is no longer to be sought
exclusively in events that come from the region of the sun. During
recent years the answer to the puzzling question of the aurora's
origin has been sought within the terrestrial sphere itself. If, in the
magnetosphere, one sees the *earth as an extended realm* as so characteristically described by Eather above, then it can be seen how, within
this terrestrial realm, solar related plasma is continually formed and

accumulated, experiences a necessary addition of energy and thus becomes that plasma which, in the encounter with denser earthly substances, is transformed into light and colour in the immediate vicinity of the earth and thus gives rise to the aurora.

It is justifiable, within the meaning of present-day science, to look for the aurora's origin in the neighbouring regions of the earth. In this case the decisive question arises as to whether the solar wind's outgoing effect is not so much the cause of the aurora as rather the occasion for an, as yet unknown, sun-related structure within the terrestrial organism, including its surrounding spheres, that gives rise to the aurora's mysterious revelation.

The progress of an aurora display is the result of a powerful expenditure of energy. The visible aurora itself represents only one thousandth of the collected and discharged energy. The energy of an average auroral display of about an hour is comparable to the energy capacity of all the man-made power-stations on earth, about a hundred million kilowatts. The magnetic storms that arise seriously affect radio communication. The occurring induction current causes corrosion on pipe-lines; at the same time this current has already been used occasionally in telephone installations for the communication of news. To what extent this powerful energy can be controlled and used by man is a genuine and dramatic question for the future.

The supersensory and electrical powers that to begin with were seen as in the hands of the gods — for example in the lightning wielded by the Greek god Zeus — have over the millenia been transferred to human hands. Will a similar occurrence with regard to the aurora take place in the future? Even now, the aurora has challenged human beings to comprehensive efforts in the search for knowledge and has thereby led them to new important insights into the relationship between the cosmos and the earth.

5. The sun — planet and fixed star

The aurora directs the researcher's attention to occurrences in the realm of the sun. The plasma radiating from this body exhibits a process which is an expression of the whole visible and measurable solar organization. This can be seen as a fourfold structure: the surface layer of the sun (the photosphere): the flaming flare immediately around the sun (the chromosphere): the surrounding aura of light (the corona); the solar plasma filling interplanetary space (the solar wind). The sun's interior, which is neither perceptible nor directly measurable, is not considered here. It was only the recent discovery of the solar plasma that led to a clear understanding of this fourfold solar organization.

Since the onset of the scientific age, the visible solar ball has been accepted as the real sun. Rightly so. For it is from the surface of this body – the photosphere – that the forces of light and warmth issue to generate life on earth. When the sun sinks below the horizon, the rays of light disappear into the heights, and darkness and coldness spread over the earth. No other part of the widely extended and intensely energetic solar organization is able, at the present time, to replace the occurrences which take place on the surface of the solar body. On it, the solar processes have a form that exhibits an affinity with terrestrial processes. Thus physical light and physical warmth are able to generate terrestrial life. Beyond this, it is the visible occurrences on the photosphere — the sunspot activity — which make possible essential disclosures about the physical and spatial-temporal constitution of the sun and at the same time they establish the connection with the aurora shining in the earth's darkness.

The dark sunspots are openings on the surface of the photosphere. In the lower stratum of this torn surface, deeper layers of the sun become visible. They are immediately below the photosphere and belong to the so-called convection zone in which arise those formations which then, as mighty granules, form the sun's surface. On the way through the convection zone, the photosphere's granulated surface is formed. Measurements have shown that the dark spot portions are significantly cooler than the surrounding surface. Seen from the earth, the spots on the sun appear small, but in terrestrial terms they are gigantic. The dark nuclei of the spots (the umbra) have an average diameter of about 20 000 km (12 500 miles), with the surrounding lighter penumbra about 50 000 km (30 000 miles). Such dimensions are many times greater than the earth's diameter. The largest group of sunspots photographed were those of 1947. They attained a diameter of over 300 000 km (200 000 miles) — almost the distance from the earth to the moon.

After an interval of sunspot absence a new phase of sunspot formation begins. The sunspots originate in high latitudes (40° to 60°) on the solar disc. Through the sun's rotation the spots move from east to west. They approach the solar equator with increasing frequency, also forming groups. Their formation lasts from two to three weeks, occasionally for several months in the case of larger groups. The spots arise in pairs at somewhat the same distance north and south of the solar equator and are accompanied by very strong magnetic fields; the pairs of spots are in themselves magnetically polarized (from one spot period to the next the polarization of the spot-pair is reversed). Somewhere in the region of latitude 15° the spot formation reaches its greatest extent and then, as it draws closer to the equator, disappears again.

Plate 15. *The aurora with its dynamic movements behaves in the heavens rather as water does on earth and as collections of stars do in the cosmos, often forming various kinds of spirals and whirlpools. The latest measurements have shown that the inner fine structure of the aurora has a spiral character. Separate appearances have been called 'curls'. The foldings and unfoldings have a breadth of about 1 km, with some 5 km (3 miles) between each. Hence the great spirals merely uncover the prevailing inner fine structure of the aurora.*

5. THE SUN — PLANET AND FIXED STAR

Between one spot maximum and the next there is a duration of between nine and thirteen years, on average somewhat over eleven years. As a rule, the expansion of the spots is much more rapid than their decrease; because of this, the graphical curve of the number of spots in time rises steeply and forms, with its even falling off, a sharp point at the maximum. Hence, it shows an impulse image. Rhythmically, this means that the time from minimum to maximum takes only about three years; the time of its dying away about eight years. The Swiss astronomer Rudolf Wolf (1826–93) made a count of sunspot cycles, beginning with the year 1755. Particularly high sunspot activity in our century was in 1917; then increasing in 1937 and 1946 until the century's maximum in December 1957. Large portions of the sun were strewn with gigantic spots. In 1976 a new sunspot cycle began, which reached an unexpected climax in the summer of 1982, comparable to that of 1957. The greater part of the aurora photographs in this book were taken during the time of this last cycle.

The increase and decrease of the sunspots is accompanied by other occurrences on the photosphere and in the transition to the chromosphere. In the immediate vicinity of the spots particular eruptions of fiery solar substances take place — the flares. They are short-lived radiation eruptions, whose duration is between minutes and, at most, an hour. Widespread flaming eruptions are continually taking place on the sun; they are visible in the thick flaming surface of the chromosphere surrounding the photosphere. Immense formations tower up within this as so-called protuberances. There are arc formations often many hundreds of thousands of kilometres in length. The specific eruptions of 'flares', however, take place in immediate connection with the spots and represent a heightened solar activity.

The spots and spot groupings move, together with the solar rotation, from east to west. As a consequence of the increasingly new spot formation in lower latitudes, the general picture is of a

Plate 16. The aurora's arcs and bands can spread out so widely that as thin veils of colour they are drawn over a large part of the sky. In that case all the colours of the spectrum can arise. Starlight penetrates the veils and reaches the earth. In this picture, on the left around the dark twin poles the constellation of Orion can be recognized. High on the right, above the lit-up transmission mast of Kiruna, is the constellation of the Bull.

movement of the spots from northeast to southwest towards the equator and, correspondingly in the southern hemisphere, from southeast to northwest. The far-stretching protuberance arcs reach out from the equatorial region to the northeast and southeast respectively; that is in the opposite direction to the spots. This comprehensive counter-movement indicates a compensatory process.

When the telescope was invented around 1600, the sunspots could clearly be seen. This perception caused a profound shock to the souls of Christian researchers and thinkers in Western Europe. When the Jesuit father, Christoph Scheiner (1575–1650) reported this revolutionary discovery to his father superior, he in his perplexity could only refer to Aristotle; he read Aristotle through from beginning to end and found nothing about spots; they could, therefore, only be ascribed to a fault in Scheiner's glasses or his eyes.

The shock felt upon clear observation of the sunspots arose from the depths of the human soul. It was justifiable that the sun should be experienced as a pure illuminating foundation of being. These dark patches appeared not only to threaten the sun but also the being closely related to it. Added to this is the fact that, until quite recently, since the discovery of these spots, there has been no suggestion of a scientific theory to explain their appearance.

In recent years important views have been formulated which put forward fundamental phenomena and thoughts towards the clarification of the sunspots' origin. J. V. Evans describes the present state of research as follows (1982, 468):

> In the convection zone the energy density of the gas motion greatly exceeds that of the solar magnetic field, and thus the motions tend to organize the fields. (Whenever the energy density of the ionized particles in space greatly exceeds that of the magnetic field, the field must follow the particle motions as if frozen into the medium.) The reverse is true in the chromosphere and corona, where the motion of the completely ionized gas is confined and controlled by the magnetic field. Sunspots are thought to be cool regions where the magnetic fields at the photosphere are strong enough to influence the convective motions and upward flow of heat. The 11-year cycle in their number and latitude on the disk may be a result of an observed differential rotation of the convection zone with latitude; the equatorial regions rotate faster than the poles. This differential motion is thought to twist the sun's dipoles

field until loops or knots of field lines break through the photosphere.

Sunspots constitute one of the biggest riddles for modern astronomy and solar-astronomy. To find a solution, the sun must be considered as a whole. Here is a fundamental question which could arise only in modern times: how is the sun to be defined; is it a planet (moving luminary) or a fixed star? As is known, planets are round, self-contained bodies and have no own source of light. The moon is the most obvious example. The sun is surrounded by a number of such moving luminaries which, together with the sun, form the planetary system in which our earth is also a planet. The present outermost boundary of this sytem is the orbit of the planet Pluto which is forty times further from the sun than the earth. The fixed stars, on the other hand, lie at incomparably greater distances from the sun. They are self-luminous and approximately motionless; even with the most powerful telescope, the fixed stars cannot be seen to have any size or form such as a regular spherical shape. The fixed stars are, above all, radiating light phenomena which appear to the human eye only as points of light; hence without any planet-like self-contained form.

It is true that photometric investigations (measurement of light values) of double stars, stars circling round each other, together with calculations of slowly progressing fixed star movements such as that of Sirius, show that these stars, too, have a structure similar to the sun. These investigations are further confirmed by spectroscopic measurements which show, on the basis of the accompanying Doppler effect, that one part of the star moves away from the observer while another part moves towards the observer, as is the case of the rotating sun. These observations suggest a relationship between the fixed stars and our sun. At the same time, however, they tempt one to make a one-sided identification.

In earlier times it was self-evident that the sun was a planet belonging to the other planetary bodies. This was not an expression of ignorant naïvety that had as yet no actual knowledge of the stars; it was an immediate experience of being. Even when the sun was regarded as a special moving luminary, its connection with the other planets was so important that this acquiescent relationship allowed it to appear as a planet. The sun's and moon's exact conformity in size and shape, evident at an eclipse of the sun, fitted the sun naturally into the roundelay of the planets. Thus the relationship, but also the diverseness, between sun and planets is essential for our planetary system. Both reveal themselves in the manifold pattern of their movements and ultimately in the origin of life. A similar occurrence in the starry universe is not known to us.

In what follows, the term 'star' is used not only to designate the random body of a star but the comprehensive, widespread radiating process in the whole of its circumference which, somewhat as a changing sun corona, is visible also in our own solar system. We may imagine, particularly on the basis of present-day partial identification of sun and fixed star, that the universe is permeated by such widely distributed plasmic occurrences. Today, increasing attention is being given to these. In what follows, these occurrences will be called *expanding star-processes*, corresponding in many respects, to the original soul experiences which human beings can have of the stars as environmental influences and effects of the spheres. In connection with light and heat activities these star-processes possess the irradiation and greatest possible dissolution of all substances to the extent of forming holes and spatial vacuums.

As a polarity to this is the *planetary condensing-process*; this arises through the occurrence of self-forming, self-contained bodies of regular spheroid shape. To this belongs the fusion of substantiality which is clearly related to terrestrial substances. In the planetary-process these substances appear in different degrees of concentration.

The peculiar position of the sun consists, therefore, in its being at one and the same time both a fixed star and a planet, thus uniting opposites within itself. It is a fixed star because through intense light and heat activity it dissolves all substantiality in extraterrestrial space, though still within our planetary system, thereby bringing about hollow-space processes. At the same time, the sun is a planet in so far as it takes on a spatially extended and also a concentrated substantial spherical form. In the whole of the sun's organization, star and planetary process encounter each other continually. They meet — concentrated above all in the photosphere — in powerful penetration and are held in a harmonious state of balance by a mutual exchange of forces and substances.

The closed harmony of planet and star opens and leads to a dissonance in the sunspot active phase. The sight of these darkened places in the sun alarmed men and easily led to a false conclusion in thought and soul: to an image of a threatening darkness and an extinction of the sun. However, the luminous photosphere as a whole does not lose in brilliancy on account of the dark spots. The sunspots, together with their margins, are surrounded by broad marginal zones in which there is an eruptive activity of particularly bright flares. The area of such a flare-field is twenty to forty times greater than the enclosed umbra (the dark centre) of a sunspot. Here there is a surplus of flaring brilliance that compensates for the light absence from the spots. The solar disc, therefore, shows no sign of decreasing light, not even a loss of heat, for the flares and flare-processes compensate for the spots' loss of heat.

These compensatory processes are confirmed by the very slight fluctuations in the solar constant (the amount of energy arriving per square centimetre per minute on earth from the sun), as measured at the atmospheric perimeter (Unsöld 1955, 593). Recent satellite measurements have shown that in these fluctuations there are tendencies to an increase and decrease of the solar constant with increasing and decreasing activity. But these changes, too, are immediately balanced by the solar energy welling up from within. Only a slight fluctuation of one thousandth of the solar constant would produce far-reaching climatic changes (Evans 1982, 469). On the other hand, however, the surface of the sun itself undergoes a transformation in the sunspot phase. In the rupturing of the sunspots, the solar surface opens towards the interior; in the flares and eruptions it is drawn outwards. This process, forming hollow cavities in the star's condition, dispersing and tearing apart the surface, becomes visible; the planetary form begins to disintegrate and pass over into another state.

If this process were to continue the sun would be transformed into a flaring brilliant fixed star before our very eyes. This would be disastrous for our earth and planetary system. Such an idea makes us aware of what it means that a cosmic star-power has taken on the form of our sun and sustains this condition in rhythmic fluctuation and dramatic altercation. This belongs to the mystery of its being, whereby it develops the power to be the outer centre of our planetary system. By means of this hollow-space star-process in the generation of the sunspots, the sun reveals that it can be fully converted into the condition of a fixed star. This would be premature at the present time, and therefore justifiably alarms people.

The recent results of solar research show impressively that the sunspot rhythm presents a transition from one light-process to another. When the solar surface is free of spots, the blue part of the spectrum, coming from the interior, predominates. At maximum sunspot activity the red part predominates. In the latter case, the solar process moves in the direction of the red light of the chromosphere and is thereby directed outward. In this case, the radiated energy is also transferred insignificantly from the blue to the red light (Holweger 1982).

In the photosphere's alternating rhythm between being free of sunspots and filled with sunspots, the sun demonstrated in time what is already discernible in space as a duality of planet and star. Planet-process and star-processes alternate in an incalculable living rhythm and thus produce the sublime solar equilibrium. In the photosphere's star-process phase, the solar wind is particularly intensive; it wafts through the planetary system and produces widespread tensions in the terrestrial magnetosphere; thus does the aurora arise on the earth's circumference.

Further confirmation of the occurrence of solar equilibrium is revealed in the observation of the sun's corona which could earlier be perceived only during a total solar eclipse. The corona appears as a bright but delicate light surrounding the darkened solar disc in varying extension and form. Today, this phenomenon can be observed without a solar eclipse. The coronagraph is a telescope with a built-in arrangement whereby it is possible to cover the sun's photosphere by optical means. Through the coronagraph the obser-vation of the sun's corona is facilitated for research and enables an exact comprehension of the changing corona.

As we know, light is visible only on and through a medium. Light itself is invisible and needs the aid of a substance in order to appear. The image of the corona's light arises through interaction with the fine interplanetary material which is distributed round the sun in varying densities. The light shining from the sun's photo-sphere makes the interplanetary material luminous whereby the various impressive forms of the corona appear, thus disclosing what-ever processes are taking place in the wider space of the sun. During the greatest sunspot activity — that is, when the expanding star-process on the photosphere develops — the corona encloses the solar sphere like a luminous spherical flower. On the other hand, when the photosphere again attains its spotless, radiating planetary form, the corona spreads out, winged and starlike, far into planetary space and can reach to the earth.

During spot-formation the corona configurations show a closed contraction; only round the poles do they open up in radiating forms. When the photosphere has few or no spots, they show an open expansion. Thus arise the conditions of systole (contraction) and diastole (expansion). The sun shows a compensatory movement: if the star-process begins to develop more vigorously on the photo-

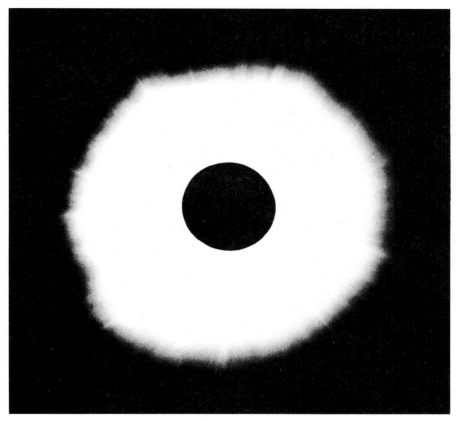

Figure 15. In this picture the sun's corona shows the spherical form typical of maximum sunspot activity. At the same time it reveals the impressive size of this corona, showing that the planetary condensing-process of the corona is active even at a great distance from the surface of the sun. The expansion of the corona to its maximum visible size is subject to strong oscillations.

sphere and chromosphere, then the corona adopts a planetary, round, enclosing form; it thus encloses the solar sphere until the sun has again closed up its torn surface and so re-established the planetary figure. The corona, having entered this phase, then evolves a star-process; it radiates out into planetary space and forms the star-like balance to the consolidated, planetary solar sphere. With reference to the fluctuating corona form, J. V. Evans writes (1982, 467f):

> Near sunspot minimum the corona often exhibits considerable gross structure, with irregular equatorial extensions,

Figure 16. Because the inner part of the corona is some ten thousand times brighter than the outer part — the starlike rays that stream far out — the corona form cannot be captured by an individual photograph. At a quite early date endeavours were made to render in drawings the impressive aurora phenomena. The above picture was taken from a photograph of the solar eclipse of January 22, 1898, five years after a powerful sunspot maximum. The picture therefore shows a form typical of sunspot minimum, where the streams of the outer corona can be seen stretching out to a distance of fifteen sun-radii. In the picture the axis of the sun is vertical.

and may be nearly absent above the poles. Near sunspot maximum the corona appears to be much more structured and jagged, but overall exhibits greater spherical symmetry.

In considering these equalizing processes of the photosphere and chromosphere on the one hand, and of the corona on the other, the image arises of a breathing process in the sun. The maximum sunspot display represents the inhaling sun. As in the case of human respiration, this solar 'breathing in' is also quicker than the 'breathing out'. The star-processes in the corona's periphery are taken up by the sun in the systole — the 'breathing in' — giving rise to intensive fire which, through instances of spots and flares, tear apart the photosphere's surface, allowing greater quantities of solar plasma to flow into the planetary environment. The earth reacts

Figure 17. This photograph of a total solar eclipse, of February 16, 1980, reveals with unusual clarity the sun-process described in the text. The eclipse occurred at the time of the most recent sunspot maximum. The picture does not show the spherical, flower-like form of the corona described in the text, for it was taken with a camera specially adapted for red light (exposure 24 seconds). Through this technique the fine structure of the corona is made visible, for the brighter light of the spherical form is cut out. This fine structure shows itself to have a regular star-shape, which makes it impossible to determine the sun's poles by the formations of the polar corona. Hence the picture shows that at sunspot maximum during the planetary condensation-process the inner character of the corona is still starlike. In its expansive working into the photosphere (and out again) this character is revealed in the sunspots. Hence they bring to expression the 'becoming-a-star' aspect of the sun.

Figure 18. A photograph during the solar eclipse of June 30, 1973, during a phase of sunspot minimum. Characteristic of this phase are the widely spread out asymmetric, winglike and starlike forms of the corona. They can range out over distances as great as that to the earth and so fill a large part of the solar system. This phase of the corona can be described as a more expansive 'star-process'.

to this more intensive star condition of the photosphere by spreading its auroral oval strongly towards the equator. The aurora discloses how the earth within solar space expresses itself in the plasma's radiating and spreading star-process. It can also be looked at from the point of view of the magnetosphere, in which case the question arises whether solar and terrestrial processes can here be regarded as at all separate.

Should the solar surface now return to the sunspot minimum,

then the sun accomplishes its 'breathing out.' The corona radiates out into the universe of the stars. At the same time, the aurora recedes over the earth. Recent measurements and photographs have shown that in the corona, too, there are hollow spaces similar to the sunspot 'holes'. These hollow structures appear to have a semi-permanent area of concentration in the sun's polar regions during the sunspot minimum. They diminish during an increase in spot formation. The growth of the sunspots in the neighbourhood of the sun's polar regions is immediately linked to this hollowing process (coronal 'holes').

On earth, the aurora is correspondingly at home in the polar regions; it is an expression of solar-related star processes. Equally, the hollow structures in the sun's polar regions are an expression of further cosmic star-processes. These go directly over into the solar wind, particularly through the holes which are formed in extensive areas of the sun's corona. Through these terrestrial-solar correspondences a cosmically connected solar-terrestrial organism becomes perceptible through the auroral process.

Recent research, shown in the results of the American-German *Helios* spacecraft program, have suprisingly shown that the solar wind itself has 'holes' which are completely devoid of solar plasma. This unexpected discovery of further hollow-structures confirms and broadens the picture given here of the sun's complementary 'expanding star-process'. In every sphere of the fourfold sun organism the pesence of the hollow structures can now be found, assuming the manifold presence of these structures in the turbulent movement of the chromosphere where the intensive fire-processes within a concentrated sphere still make direct measurement difficult or impossible.

Research into the solar plasma is becoming more and more extensive at the present time. The largest amount of matter in space consists of plasma similar to that of the sun. The well-known Japanese auroral researcher Syuin-Ichi Akasofu writes:

> Therefore, this extreme condition of matter is of
> fundamental importance to an understanding of almost
> every aspect of astronomy, such as the formation of the
> solar system, various processes in the sun, stars, quasi-
> stellar objects, pulsars and galaxies. The auroral plasma is
> the only one in nature that can be studied *directly* by
> satellite-borne instruments (except for information gathered
> by occasional visits of space probes to some of the other
> planets) . . . (1979, 87).

> . . . Some auroral scientists believe that basic plasma
> processes associated with solar flares are similar to those of
> auroral phenomena. Some also believe that by studying the
> auroral plasma we can better understand how the solar
> system evolved, since it must have been formed by
> contraction of a huge plasma cloud. (1979, 39).

Akasofu's words contain decisive indications. They show the aurora as a window on hitherto hidden mysteries of the solar system. These begin to be elucidated when the individual members of the solar organization are looked at in the light of Anthroposophy against the background of evolution. The appearance of the form that has been described in referring to the planetary bodies, in particular the solar body, is an expression of the present existential state of our world as immediately surveyed. Ultimately, the immense profusion of form structures in all realms of nature can be understood as foundation and expression of the earth's being only when one looks back on the creation and phases of creation. In this respect, it is expected that the solar organization, particularly with its plasmic occurrences recently made accessible to us, will show immediate traces of the creational phases. The creative forces that lead to the origin of the world of forms issue forth from beings. In terms of Anthroposophy (founded by Rudolf Steiner) they are called Spirits of Form and stand at the beginning of creation's acts. In earlier times they were experienced and recognized as a multiplicity of beings. In the Jewish tradition it is these spirits which, at the beginning of Genesis, the Bible enumerates in the plural as *Elohim* (later Greek: *Exousiai*). The choir of the Elohim is the creator of our present world, discernible in the seclusion of the appearing forms. This world condition can be described, in terms of Anthroposophy, as the 'planetary earthly state'. To this also belongs the surrounding planetary bodies with the sun and its visible photosphere. The immediate relationship of this part of the sun with the earth is obvious. The earth is only aroused to light, warmth and life when the sun itself rises above the horizon. The specific photosphere occurrences could not be replaced by any plasmic starlike activities, no matter how extensive and intensive they were. Thus it is also in the region of the photosphere, through observations of sunspots, that the actual physical regularities, such as the rotation of the sun, have been perceived. Eventually, the activity of the Spirits of Form leads to the filling of the world of forms with physical mineral substances. Traces of this occurrence can be discerned in the photosphere.

5. THE SUN — PLANET AND FIXED STAR

However, one can look further back than merely to the 'planetary earth state'. Anthroposophy speaks of a previous phase of creativity as of an 'ancient moon state' or Old Moon. This has no direct relationship with the present planetary lunar body, for this, in the sense of what has been said above, is also an expression of the present state of the earth. During the ancient moon state, final fixed forms had not yet arisen. The activity of *movement* predominated, though the world of form was already arising. Thus one can discern a half-formed primordial world where intensive dynamic occurrences were working shapingly within and on an incipient world of forms. In a description of this phase of creation, Rudolf Steiner (1861–1925) has a passage (1979, 146f):

> To the supersensible observer of these processes, it is as
> though organs were opening out and drawing to again,
> while a warmth-giving stream pours in and out of them,
> and air and water substances are conveyed inwards and
> outwards . . . Manifold processes are taking place within
> [the vapour-like environment]. Substances are combining,
> substances are separating; some parts grow more condensed,
> others thin out, become more tenuous.

All these described occurrences in the planetary moon condition are to be perceived, in altered form, within the sun's chromosphere. The flame-like phenomena — often comparable to burning cornfields — constitute forms that are always coming and going. They spread round the sun like a wave-tossed sea, out of which the violent protuberances rise up as gigantic arcs of fire and bridge distances that surpass any earthly standard, filling spaces that correspond to the sphere of the moon. They penetrate surrounding regions of the sun where lightness and heaviness appear to be held in balance and where with regard to perceptions, the question arises as to whether the fire substances originate only in the solar body itself or come from the sun's circumference (corona), condense on the protuberances and there 'drip' off. These extremely dynamic events convey the image of powerfully active beings which can be called 'Spirits of Movement', (Greek: *Dynameis*). The chromosphere presents an image of the events in which these hierarchical beings unceasingly convert the enclosed form of the solar sphere into other unformed states and also guide the other occurrences in the solar environment to the forms of the photosphere. The light-filled corona becomes visible as a *changing form-structure* through the finely distributed cosmic matter around the sun. The dynamic transitions of the different corona structures point to further, invisible, processes whose energetic character works in the widths of interplanetary space and can there be measured. Readings of incredibly high temperatures (millions of degrees) are made here in contrast to the much lower surface temperatures of about 6000° C (11 000° F). These are, of course, only theoretical temperatures, nevertheless they indicate a significant process. It is the transition from a lower, concentrated, solar warmth to high energy and expansive *movement processes* which at the same time always keep an element of form. In that the corona is a visible-invisible structure of light it can show the way to the real substance of light which — like light itself — is not sensory and can thus lead to the supersensory. The corona heat is only discernable indirectly, it has semi-supersensory characteristics and can thus also make a connection with the supersensory.

The sun's corona is the lofty and radiant expression of the mighty sun's aura which has been known and held in high estimation since ancient times. With respect to the macrocosmic human being at the 'planetary sun state' or the 'Old Sun' Rudolf Steiner describes (1979, 131) the transition from the peaceful, resting 'Saturnian' warmth-substance to the formative dynamic processes where, similar to the corona, a comprehensive warmth mantle is formed.

> Within the warmth-substance delicate, tenuous structures
> emerge, which are brought into regular movement by the
> forces of the life-body. These structures make manifest the
> physical body of the human being as it is at this stage in
> its evolution. They are permeated through and through
> with warmth, and are also enveloped as if by an
> integument of warmth. Warmth-creations with air-forms
> incorporated in them, the latter engaged in regular and
> constant movement — so may we describe the human
> being, physically speaking, at this stage.

The correspondence of the corona-process with this old state is further clarified by a significant occurrence which is common to both. It is perceivable in the changing corona-form how, during *one* phase (at sunspot maximum), this concentrates towards the centre by enveloping the solar ball itself like a sphere, and in *another* (minimum) it opens up starlike to the surrounding universe. The corona-process moves at one time in the direction of the sun's interior, at another time in the direction of outer space.

A corresponding occurrence is to be found in the old, very much greater sphere of the sun. In this case, the transition from warmth and movement strides further into light. This occurrence is accomplished by the hierarchical beings, the 'Spirits of Wisdom' (in Greek, *Kyriotetes*, the 'Masters' or 'Lords'). Wisdom and light are two manifestations of the activity of these beings. In a lecture on this subject, Steiner explains (1953, 31f [1911 Nov 7]):

> Let us imagine the Spirits of Wisdom situated at the centre of the Sun absorbed in contemplation of the vision of the sacrificing Thrones [even higher hierarchical beings]; and by reason of this vision, radiating forth their own being; and receiving back their radiating being which they sent forth, receiving it reflected back from the surface [from the inside of the surrounding sphere], so that they receive it back as light. Everything is illuminated. What then do they receive back? Their own being surrendered by them became a gift to the Macrocosm, it was their inner being. Now it rays back to them; their own being meets them coming back from outside . . .
>
> The inner and the outer are the two opposites which we now meet . . . and 'Space' is born!

In this sense, the present sun's corona-process can be seen as having arisen in our planetary earth-state as an image of the Old Sun events. In the corona, energetic warmth processes generate a space-filling occurrence of light in the fluctuation between inward and outward going.

The solar wind, with the solar plasma, issues from the events within the corona without transition. It streams through the whole planetary system and fills it. Planetary space remains dark, for the plasma is not light and not even, like the corona, light-related. On the contrary, this stream of ions and protons is related to matter. The solar wind carries ionized material particles, such as hydrogen and helium, along with it, and moves with fluctuating velocity according to the force of its expulsion and the opposition it encounters. Its relationship to all material substance is demonstrated in its being bound to magnetic forces. The plasma carries along these forces which, on the photosphere, are already all-embracingly and intensively united with the sunspots. In this way, the direction of the plasmic stream is diverted from the magnetic fields of other planets. As plasma in the earth's magnetosphere, it produces light and colour in the terrestrial darkness in the form of the aurora, by colliding with highly refined terrestrial matter.

The solar wind fills a planetary space which was once occupied by a yet earlier creative phase than the 'Old Sun' state; it is the space reaching to present-day Saturn. (It is known that the solar wind penetrates to the trans-Saturnian planets, Uranus, Neptune and Pluto.) Hence the solar wind-process can be regarded as a later, present-day expression of a still earlier phase of creation, that of 'Old Saturn'. In this very first realm of creation, the ground was laid for the rise of material substance. 'Old Saturn' was an even darker world-body, but within this body a glimmering play of light begins (Steiner 1979, 122):

> A life of light begins, flickering here and there within the
> Saturn world and dying down again. At some places a
> quivering of glowing light will appear, at others something
> more like rapid lightning-flashes. The Saturn warmth-
> bodies begin to glimmer and glisten, even to radiate light.

The agreement of this exposition with descriptions of the aurora is striking. The streaming solar wind conceals embryonically within it — combined with and tied to material occurrences — primordial, light substance. Under certain conditions, it then comes into terrestrial space as aurora and produces the overwhelming profusion of light and colour phenomena; they are like a shining echo of the far distant past when the arising form-phantoms on Old Saturn were preparing our physical-mineral creation.

These correlations throw a crucial light on the fact that the aurora is rightly called the 'cold light'. It is in fact not completely cold, but in relationship to the development of energy and colour, the ascertained temperatures are astonishingly low. The germinating light of Old Saturn is comparable to the first light of dawn before sunrise. That, too, is cold. The dark body of old Saturn bore warmth within itself, but warmth that was still bound to darkness. The light arising had not yet gone through the next stage of 'Old Sun' in which the dark warmth transformed into actually generating light and was combined with it.

To begin with, therefore, only a faint warmth issued from the Saturn light. Similarly, with the aurora, while the arising gleam of the latent supersensory primordial light originated in the first creation of Old Saturn, the colour display of the complete solar spectrum flared up as a result of the following Sun creation and later phases of creation ('planetary embodiments of the earth'). The earth's aurora reveals a panorama of the past creative phases of its planetary evolution, in which at the same time there lie hidden germs for the future structure of the earth.

6. On the nature of the earth

The aurora develops over the landscapes of the north and of the Antarctic continent. Although this display of light and colour has been recognized as a cosmic phenomenon, the question arises about its relationship to the terrestrial regions over which it develops. In what follows, therefore, a characterization of these regions will be given, using the northern regions as an example. An attempt will be made to put together these descriptions from the whole context of the earth's life-structure, even though this is not yet completely understood. The significance that a description of this life-structure of one part of the earth has for the aurora will be shown in some significant occurrences wherein, however, much is left open as a foundation for further understanding.

Several fundamental phenomena at latitude 60° on the earth show that here a threshold is crossed which leads into regions where, at any given time in the north or south, significantly changed conditions are met with. A number of the more important instances will now be delineated by way of introduction.

The 'light boundary' has already been mentioned. In the zone of latitude 60° the light begins to be continually present at the height of summer. A human being coming from temperate regions is not able, for instance, by sleeping and waking, to keep up with the sun's rhythm. He enters a rhythmic realm of light and darkness foreign to him. This is much more related to extra-terrestrial planetary rhythms.

It is in this very region that we find the origins of great turbulence of the air masses. They arise on the boundary of two air currents: the northern current moves pre-eminently from east to west, the current south of latitude 60° primarily from west to east. Thus there arises on this boundary a zone of friction and encounter which produces cloud formations and builds up the whole meteorological configuration. On account of these occurrences, this latitudinal zone is a source of moving and — as will be shown — living forces. In connection with this, the ocean currents demonstrate the same tendency. In the north, the extensive ice fields are carried slowly from east to west. Immense quantities of water are continually flowing from the frozen Antarctic continent. South of latitude 60° they flow predominantly in an east-west direction, while north of this latitude they flow from west to east. Finally, the frequent visibility of the aurora begins in this zone.

All these phenomena are indications of a deeper occurrence which this region's changed life-structure reveals. This, however, is hidden from the perception of the senses and lies in the supersensory; it shows itself only in its effects.

In Chapter 2 this occurrence was briefly outlined. In the prehistoric age of myth, it could be perceived clairvoyantly and described in images. The 'grinding Sampo' of the *Kalevala* is the mythical expression in images of this occult happening. On account of this hiddenness one could not, hitherto, get an insight into the reality that lay at the basis of the image. It is to Sampo that the 'many coloured lid' belongs, and it was in the enclosing form of this lofty colourful phenomenon that the central northern sky was seen, with its far-flung, many-coloured aurora against the background of the stars which shone through it. The grinding Sampo itself was sketched as an imaginatively perceived image that arose out of the continual encounter of the rotating earth with a sphere of forces that enveloped it. On the northern and southern light boundaries — latitude 60° — the impression of a grinding process arose. Towards the end of the *Kalevala* the combination of forces underlying this Sampo image is clearly indicated 'From these seeds the plant is sprouting,/ Lasting welfare is commencing,' (XLIII, 297f). The seed's origin is the supersensory realm from which life itself comes forth, a realm also called, in the terminology of Anthroposophy, the etheric world. This world of etheric forces stands in the background when the image described in what follows is called the 'sphere of forces', the 'life-sphere', of the earth.

The first appearances of this sphere of forces were ascertained scientifically over two hundred years ago and observed as mysterious, regular atmospheric pressure fluctuations. In the mornings and evenings they rise to a somewhat higher pressure; in the afternoons and after midnight to a correspondingly lower pressure. This phenomenon was later termed the 'semidiurnal pressure wave'. Up to the present time, the great number of attempts to attribute these fluctuations of atmospheric pressure to external influences, above all to daily thermal effects of the sun, have only led to partial results. Johann Wolfgang Goethe (1749–1832) also directed his attention to this mysterious phenomenon. He concluded that these atmospheric pressure fluctuations did not have their cause outside, but within the earth itself: 'We seek, therefore, the causes of the barometric changes not without, but within the earthly sphere; they are not cosmic, not atmospheric, but terrestrial.' (Wachsmuth 1965, 25). With this, Goethe became the discoverer of a hitherto unperceived life-condition of the earth, even though he still called his discovery a search.

In time, the fluctuations in atmospheric pressure came to be regarded as a global occurrence which took place with rhythmic precision, approximately along the earth's lines of longitude. The atmospheric pressure reaches its height towards nine o'clock in the morning; after that it falls again to a corresponding low point about three in the afternoon. The same thing is repeated towards nine in the evening and three in the morning. During the course of the day, all places on earth, from east to west, go through the same atmospheric pressure fluctuations. We have the impression of a wave of air pressure running twice daily round the globe of the earth. This happens quite independently of the seasons.

During increasing global observations of these rhythmic fluctuations in pressure, it was established that the crests and troughs of the pressure curves flatten out the further north and south the measurements were made on the earth. The waves showed greatest difference between maximum and minimum at the equator; at latitude 60° the difference decreases greatly, disappearing altogether at the poles. On the polar caps the atmospheric pressure is uniformly somewhat greater so that here the semidiurnal pressure wave decreases into a higher pressure level; at the poles, changes in pressure cease entirely. There is here a phenomenological indication of the sphere of forces. That it is to be regarded as a life-sphere is demonstrated by the numerous living events in the botanical, zoological and human realm, underlying which is the same rhythm of contracting and expanding forces, of systole and diastole. Here it

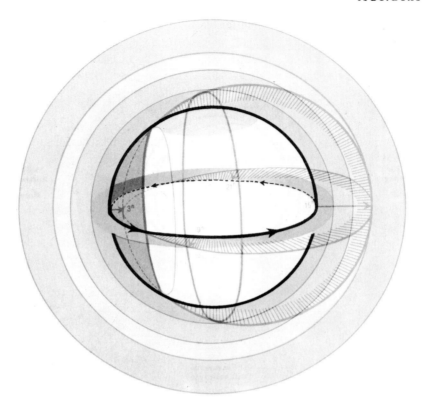

Figure 19. The sphere of forces ('respiratory sphere') of the earth-organism in the course of a day. On the left: Part of the earth (shown dark) lies at night outside the forces-sphere. On the right: the forces-sphere has breathed out and finds itself above the earth's surface in daylight. Extreme positions are at 3 am and at 3 pm.

must be emphasized that these supersensory etheric forces have the capacity, not only of stimulating living things, but also of influencing the physical occurrence of atmospheric movement. Connected with this is an abundance of meteorological effects, all of which issue from this superimposed life-rhythm. This rhythmical sphere of forces is dealt with comprehensively and in detail by Günther Wachsmuth (1893–1963), who calls it the 'respiration sphere'.

Wachsmuth constructs out of the global rhythmic phenomena of the semidiurnal atmospheric pressure wave an exact spatial image of a supersensory sphere which, being somewhat larger than the earth, surrounds it. As it is eccentrically displaced, part of the earth always lies outside the sphere of forces which faces the sun. The sphere is not aligned exactly towards the sun, so there arises a divergent angle in relation to the visible sun's position which entails a lapse of about three hours: the sun's meridian passage is at noon, the sphere's meridian passage is at three in the afternoon.

The portion of the earth outside the sphere always lies in night's darkness and so is turned away from the sun. If the sphere of forces were visible, an observer on the equator would see it coming towards him in the morning at about six o'clock like a mighty wave; this portion of the earth, coming out of the darkness, turns slowly from the west to the east carrying the observer into the life-sphere. As it ascends, the wave would, at nine o'clock, be fully visible from its inner side as a far-flung heavenly arch and would, at the same time, show its greatest rate of change, its most concentrated systole activity. The atmospheric pressure thereby reaches the culmination belonging to this phase. After this, the pressure begins to decrease slowly again, while the sphere moves further upwards. At three o'clock it reaches its highest position at about 70 km (45 miles) altitude. On the earth, the atmospheric pressure has sunk to its lowest level; it is the diastole phase of expansion.

Towards evening, the sphere of forces again sinks so far that the concentrating effects are shown anew: at nine o'clock they attain the greatest rate of change causing the same atmospheric pressure's culmination as at nine in the morning. Thereafter, the earth begins to rotate out of the sphere. This is completed about midnight, after which a portion of the sphere sinks under the earth's surface to about 23 km (14 miles). When the atmospheric pressure reaches its second lowest level, at three in the morning, its nature differs from that of the afternoon's low level in that the forces-sphere no longer surrounds the earth's surface. The sphere is a structure that arises only in the earth's continuous movement and is sustained only in continued processes that arise out of a multitude of effects.

Human life is immediately influenced, if not considerably formed inwardly, by the rhythm of the sphere of forces. In the morning hours from eight to ten o'clock, the human being develops the greatest efficiency. Towards midday, there enters a kind of crisis; the human constitution remains inwardly upright and wakeful only with difficulty. This condition lasts until about three when a distinct turning-point enters. Following this, a phase of soul-awakening begins which reaches a high point towards evening and then in the late evening fades away again. The repeated crisis at three o'clock in the night is not usually noticed by a sleeping human being. However, its presence makes itself evident in that it is a time when people often die. These rhythmical effects of the sphere of forces mould important life-processes even in the formation of the embryo and thus strongly influence the nature of the human being. They are like a pulse-beat acting from without that dovetails into the basic rhythmical framework of the human constitution.

In Central Europe, and in regions corresponding to this latitude in the Northern and Southern hemispheres, human beings live in a region of the earth where the rhythmical beat of this sphere's heights and depths is much lower than in the equatorial zone. The oscillations present a medial condition. Further north and south respectively, the heights and depths continually decrease and a broad change takes place in the relationship to the sphere of forces. If this were visible to an observer looking north in a northern latitude approaching 60°, he would see, besides the now flatter sphere's arch coming from the east, at the same time, the sphere's edge in the north-east and north moving likewise from east to west. The sphere's arc in the east rises here much more slowly and, at the afternoon's lowest pressure, reaches a lower altitude. After this, it also sinks again slowly downwards. When, at three o'clock in the morning, the earth is just turning out of the sphere's arc, the above view returns again: the immersed sphere in the north with its simultaneously arriving portion in the north-east and east. Directly below latitude 60°, therefore, the earth leaves the enveloping sphere of forces for only a short time. When it enters again, it moves away and draws nearer, gradually climbing and sinking in continual conformity with fluctuations in pressure: lowest pressure in the morning (3 am) and afternoon (3 pm) when the sphere is lowest and highest; greatest pressure during the periods between when the spherical arc is at a medium height and is changing fastest.

This low level of the sphere's cupola tends generally to a somewhat higher atmospheric pressure in this zone and to an etherically enclosed body vibrating concentratedly in itself. Its uppermost portion, situated constantly over the poles, appears as a 'lid' on this region of the earth; it forms the so-called polar caps. The *Kalevala* conception of the 'many-coloured lid' may be understood and amplified to accord with this pattern. The profound wisdom in concept-formation becomes evident within mythical language, which is so constituted that it cannot be determined by outwardly given

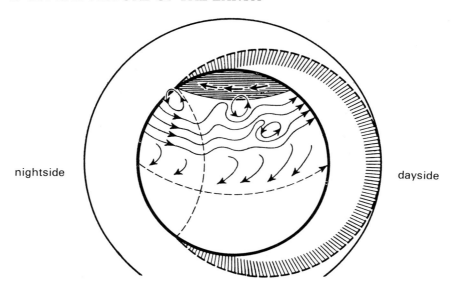

nightside

dayside

Figure 20 The formation of waves and cyclones in the general atmospheric circulation.

perceptions. In this forming of concepts or names, therefore, a supersensory condition can enter in.

The sphere that dips in at latitude 60° moves through and round the earth from east to west as a result of the earth's rotation. Hence there arises a particularly strong, active limiting process which penetrates the events of the polar cap. At the same time, the deeper lying arc of the forces-sphere causes a further concentration which gives, etherically, the whole polar cap the character of that phase of activity which further south is active only in the mornings and evenings. These are the phases of maximum deployment of the forces of the life-sphere.

This unique peculiarity of the polar cap is described by Wachsmuth as follows (1965, 161):

The cupola of forces, which is only slightly arched over the polar regions, embraces a *compressed body of air*. The effect exerted by this field of force moves in an east-west direction during the course of the day; that is to say, counter to the earth's rotation about the pole. There arises thereby a kind of circling, gliding movement around the edge of the polar cap. . . . In this way, this cupola of force *moulds* ever anew the air body contained in it with its impulses as it moves

round the polar caps. On the edge of the body of air a
contour-forming and structuring impulse occurs, while
this contoured body of air is moulded continually from
without towards the inside, plastically formed, and guided
to structural changes. The moulding activity of such spheres
of force from outside inwards presents a graphic image
of the efficacy of the formative forces described above.
These forces lead here to the formation of elastic structures
and to the fashioning of contoured organs inwardly
changeable.

Here, *grinding and plastically forming events* are described which, in
the *Kalevala*, are handed down through the special language of myth
in almost the same manner as in the Sampo story. In the imaginative
accounts, the production of different inorganic and organic structures
and substances is described during, as well as after, the Sampo
forging.

The concentrated life-processes within the polar cap are
accompanied by heightened electric and magnetic occurrences. Wherever living things arise, electricity and magnetism are incorporated;
they are a presupposition for every embodiment and also its
sequence and belong, therefore, to all terrestrial organisms.

Thus the influence of the sphere of forces in the morning also
shows a heightened electric field of tension: the electric potential
between different layers of air, and the earth's surface reaches its
maximum at this time; the same with the evening hours. The corresponding low points in the afternoons and after midnight are also
established. On the part of the earth between the polar caps, the
electric field is so radically reduced that, particularly during the
night, the vertical electrical currents discharging the potentials
between the air and the earth can be active parallel to the life sphere's
submergence in the terrestrial depths. The potential's minimum in
the night, during the full submersion of the sphere, implies a
maximum in the air's conductivity. On the other hand, when the
arc of the sphere is closer to the earth, the potential gradient within

*Plate 17. This impressive photograph, taken in November 1979, shows
parts of an arc encompassing the night sky. These arcs can stretch out over
more than 1 000 km (600 miles). Within the arc a band has built up into
a spiral as a result of intensive movements. The true extent of these
powerful arcs and spirals cannot be grasped by the human eye.*

the polar caps increase and lasts longer. The air's conductivity is correspondingly diminished; this leads to a hindrance of the vertical conductivity whereby the heightened potential remains.

Under the conditions of evening and morning, electric field processes are revealed which, at other times, are present only at higher layers of the atmosphere. The stronger fluctuations of atmospheric pressure on the earth's equatorial zone and their decrease towards the poles, applies also to the rhythms of vertical electric potential. At the same time, the decrease in the rhythm's intensity — as with air pressure — is transferred to a generally somewhat higher electric potential at the polar caps, demonstrated particularly in the transition to the well-known magnetic occurrences in the polar regions.

The magnetic fluctuations during the day also correspond to the basic rhythm of the sphere of forces. Thus the compass needle's North Pole is deflected more strongly to the east at nine o'clock in the morning; in the phase up to three in the afternoon it swings towards the west again. Fridtjof Nansen had already drawn attention to the magnetic pole's daily fluctuations, which today are known to be related to the basic rhythm of the sphere of forces.

Above all, however, the phases of changeability in the magnetic field were demonstrated. Following on from the work of Birkeland, the Norwegian Leif Harang made investigations that led to the discovery of magnetic oscillations. Harang calls them 'sinusoidal oscillations', other researchers call them 'giant micropulsations'. Their reversal occurs at three o'clock in the morning. It coincides, therefore, exactly with the turning of the submerged forces-sphere. Besides this, high points of fine magnetic oscillations are discovered at nine in the morning and nine at night. These occurrences, too, are concentrated in a peculiar manner within the polar caps. Although there is a concentration and slowing down of all processes, the independent basic rhythm of the sphere of forces remains. Even the outer spatial form of the sphere's cupola shows the essential difference, in contrast to the structure in southern terrestrial regions. While the upper boundary of the sphere of forces at the equator reaches up to 70 km (45 miles), its altitude sinks to about 45 km (30 miles) in the Central European latitudes. At latitude 60° it is then

Plate 18. A beautiful example of a spiral form taken on by a far-stretched aurora curtain (see also the caption to Plate 15).

only about 35 km (22 miles). At the pole itself, the altitude sinks to about 16 km (10 miles), where it remains fairly constant.

In the altitudes above the polar caps, the auroral ovals are formed. As they form around the geomagnetic poles, the ovals are transposed in relation to the caps. If they were centred on the poles they would be in the middle zones of the caps, somewhere between latitudes 70° and 80°. However, owing to the transposition, the auroral zone moves in relation to the earth. This movement of the auroral zone, causes the dovetailing of the aurora into the basic rhythm of the sphere of forces. The pattern in space and time of a typical auroral display begins in the early evening. At this time, the cupola of the sphere of forces, following its altitudinal turning-point at 3 pm, is significantly nearer the earth's surface. The greatest effects of the sinking sphere issue forth until midnight. This period is, as a rule, also the time of the most intensive auroral display. After midnight, the sphere is closest to the earth (being immersed in the earth below 60°); at the same time, the aurora fades. The reverse motion follows towards three in the morning and the sphere begins to rise again. This is also the magnetic turning-point with its oscillation maximum, as already mentioned.

The combination of the aurora's appearance and the forces-sphere rhythm does not directly have the same cause as the effects described within the sphere. The cause of the synchronization lies as much in the fixed relationship to the sun and in the much higher-lying auroral oval as in the forces-sphere: the basic alignment of both is to the sun. The relationship of the auroral oval to the sphere of forces is, therefore, apart from the secondary motion of the oval's displacement, by and large fixed in time and space; for, like the sphere, the oval, too, does not turn with the earth's rotation. That is how the typical auroral phenomenon arises in North America and Northern Scandinavia.

The auroral oval ring is narrow on its solar side and shows a tremendous breadth on the side turned away from the sun (see Plate 11). This conspicuous auroral phenomenon on the nightly, dark side lies, accordingly, above the lowest part of the sphere. This broad part of the oval moves from latitude 60° in North America (Hudson Bay) through 70° (north coast of Alaska) in the Arctic Ocean, stretches up to 80° (Severnaya Zemlya, North Land), passing Lapland (70°) in Northern Europe before returning south to Hudson Bay at 60°. For an observer in northern Scandinavia the auroral oval during the day appears to come from Spitsbergen (where it is always found), swinging towards northern Norway, and then at midnight, turns back again. At midday its boundary is again over Spitsbergen.

The polar cupolas of the forces-sphere are structures in which variable effects are concentrated. What nearer the equator, as a concentration of forces, can spread out extensively, is here held fast, enclosed and compressed. A concentrated tension is produced, particularly through the continuous 'grinding process' of the super-imposed layer and immersed surface of the sphere. In these forces-cupolas, etheric barrage zones are formed which have their centres in the earth's polar regions. Here, the forces that in the earth's more temperate latitudes are only apparent for a few hours during height-ened phases, are continually active. Actual low-level phases are not present; their weak impressions are obliterated by the condition of general high pressure and tension.

It can now be discerned how the particular circumstances of polar caps influence the ever-present electric field of tension between the earth's surface and the ionosphere. The almost statically closed struc-ture of forces here is quite absent in the earth's equatorial zone. Here the magnetic field lines lie parallel to the sphere's surface. In this equatorial region of the earth, therefore, the terrestrial forces and the cosmic forces are cut off from one another. By contrast in the earth's North and South there is an extreme polarization in relationship to these two structures of forces. The forces-sphere of the polar caps is maximally compressed and enclosed within itself. The magnetic field lines, on the contrary, concentrate radially at the magnetic poles, in one sense showing a tremendous concentration, while in another can be seen as radiating out and expanding from the pole into all direc-tions of space. Thus, in an intermediate region, a harmonious encounter takes place between the forces-sphere, extended by the earth's surface, and the whole high-reaching ionosphere, but also giving rise often to a dramatic clash between these polarities. The auroral process allows this encounter to appear in the realm of the visible.

It is a characteristic of the ever-impressive experiences of the aurora that it appears to display itself in the immediate terrestrial landscape, quite near to the observer. Thus it is brought into a relationship with the earth and a particular landscape in the same way that particular cloud formations belong to corresponding land-scapes. It is true that there are also auroral displays that appear at quite considerable altitudes but then, again, others that envelop mountains or seem to touch the observer. To this must be added

111

other perceptions, such as, for example, the accompanying sounds. As to whether these are subjective hallucinations or objective sounds of discharging magnetic fields is, in this case, of little importance. The observer is standing within the whole theatre of the auroral display and the peculiar etheric landscape belongs to it. He does not experience himself as separate from the aurora but percipiently and empirically involved in the event. A comparison with dreams is here relevant; the dreamer experiences events outside himself, but at the same time, he is aware that he more or less takes part in producing these events or even is the cause of them. Thus the perceptual experiences with regard to the aurora can recognize their other-worldly grandeur, but cannot confirm that occurrences at very great distances from the earth are involved.

The cosmic-terrestrial image of the auroral process is becoming clearer. The shining auroral ovals take form as light and colour blossoms above the earth's polar regions. Into the centres of these blossom-structures pale red solar plasma flows from the high realms of the sun. It fills the chalice structure, invisible to the naked eye, with solar processes which pass out of the heights into the depths. The oval chalices themselves are formed out of the plasma processes, which penetrate the earth from the wide circle of the self-enclosed magnetosphere. The buckled and folded vertical walls of these chalices — the mighty auroral curtains — are thereby stretched many hundreds of kilometres downward and upward. It is these, above all, which are perceived as individual phenomena in the earth's auroral landscape.

The auroral chalice grows narrower below as it follows the field lines which converge on the geomagnetic pole. The forces-structures of these field lines connect the auroral ovals with the specific magnetic structures of the polar regions and their life-processes. They open them up, as it were, just as the stalks of flowers, submerged in the soil, open up the earthly realm in the rooting process. At the same time, however, material processes react upwards on the paths of the field lines into the auroral chalices (for example, atoms of oxygen and nitrogen.) Within the blossom-like oval structures themselves (that is, not in the polar centres of these structures) a profusion of forms come and go in a glowing and radiating wealth of colour. They form on the mobile geomagnetic field and the particular configuration of the earth's substance which is present here, through which the profusion of colour also arises.

The floating blossom-ovals expand and contract rhythmically and in spontaneous succession, in conjunction with the sunspot rhythm and consequent eruptive plasma-expansions in the magnetosphere. Thus, particularly wide extensions of the oval-blossoms give rise to a visible aurora over the whole earth. In this way, the oval-chalices continually make solar activity and terrestrial processes manifest. These extremely dynamic events could be brought about as moving, shining, colourful formations only through the magnetic fields of the sun and the earth. It is, therefore, characteristic when Wachsmuth describes the significance of magnetism in the following words (1965, 215):

> The study of magnetism is instructive for our conception of the world, because we are here concerned with an operation that does not have the monotonous uniformity of gravity, for at the basis of magnetic phenomena there are great variations during the course of the day, and so on. However, there is also not such a turbulent and disintegrating effect as with, for example, heat, but in magnetism there is present a unifying, co-ordinating tendency with great mobility in a living manner. Gravity tends to only draw things together, heat tends to dissolve; gravity alone would lead to a conglomeration and stagnation, heat alone to chaos. Magnetism tends towards unification and yet allows thereby for variation and mobility. At the same time, it is directive and therefore regulating and formative and thus a many-sided aid in the arranging of the earth's organism.

These cosmic-terrestrial effects of magnetism are made to appear brilliantly in unique beauty in the earth's darkness.

7. Lightning, rainbow, aurora

Lightning, rainbows and the aurora form light and colour phenomena within the earth's environment. All three are embedded in the encircling blue of the earth's surrounding atmosphere, from the black-blue of the thunder-cloud, the bright daylight blue of the rainbow to the midnight blue forming a background to the aurora. With the last the sunlight itself does not appear; it is invisible. Brightness and darkness are visible, and above all, the spectrum colours. Apart from the sun itself, it is the surrounding atmospheric blue that most strongly transmits the light and with it the brightness.

The all-embracing natural affinity of lightning, rainbows and aurora was first described by Walter Bühler (1972). This comprehensive account makes an attempt to grasp the three different light phenomena as actual metamorphoses of sunlight. Much of the following leans on this account but here the evolutionary aspect is placed in the foreground.

In the lightning's dominating power, early man saw the display of higher divine forces. As a result of this insight, the Greeks represented their highest god, Zeus, as the Lightning Thrower. What was seen in earlier times as a divine act, is seen by present-day man as an electrical phenomenon. However, the actual genesis of lightning is in this scientific age still hidden in obscurity, although the electric power that accompanies lightning has been taken out of the hands of the gods and put to pragmatic use.

114

7. LIGHTNING, RAINBOW, AURORA

Lightning has its origin in the clouds; its beginning must be sought in a particular process of cloud formation. The particular clouds can best be observed in tropical regions where they give rise, often daily, to thunderstorms with their lightning phenomena. In these regions the sun's rays penetrate almost vertically to the earth's surface and heat it up fiercely. This results in strong rising currents of expanded and therefore lighter, hot air. During this ascent hot air streams from all sides. The air's powerful updraughts accelerate and can attain speeds of up to 30 metres per second (70 miles per hour).

Close to the ground, the hot air absorbs large quantities of moisture which it takes up into high altitudes. In ascending, however, the air cools and is no longer able to carry the moisture. It condenses and is released as water vapour; the cloud begins to form. The more moisture taken up and released the greater the cloud formation. Then we get the characteristic cumuli and later the cumulo-nimbus clouds — the thunderstorm clouds which tower up in tremendous swollen formations. The cooling increases steadily on the way upward; with each kilometre the temperature falls initially by about 10° C (5.5° F per 1000 feet) but decreasing at higher altitudes to 3° C per km (1.6° F/1000 ft). Depending on thermal conditions, freezing-point is reached at a height of about five kilometres (3 miles).

In the ascending current which has become a kind of stem of the cloud formation, due to particular dynamic conditions, the ascending vapour can become supercooled, that is, still fluid even at temperatures below freezing point. When it finally does freeze, numerous ice crystals are formed, some of which scatter upwards in tenuous particles. Only then, when this condition has been reached, does lightning flash from the cloud. It has attained its decisive point of maturity in which snow, sleet and hail are engendered. The thunderclouds continue to build up powerfully, whereby the various processes become even more intensive.

The structure of the great cumulo-nimbus thunder clouds, with their anvil of umbrella formations, can be regarded from various points of view: meteorologically as a turbulence, thermodynamically as a heat machine or as an electrical generator. All these points of view are unable to grasp the origin of lightning, for they are the effects of an event which at first can be grasped only pictorially in an organic context. Even the gradual growth of the cumulus cloud resembles the growth of a flower or tree. As through a network of roots, the hot air is sucked up from all sides, the puffed up, horizontal accumulations of cloud that spread out from the 'trunk' (often spread out and floating on layers of air) are an image of a foliage formation.

Then, in high altitudes, the cloud rises into a flower formation; this is a consequence of the ice crystallizing process. Thus the whole formation of a thunder-cloud shows a tendency common to all forms of nature — a tendency to polarize into the opposite conditions. A plant is polarized into flower and root, a human being into head and limbs.

The appearances of polarization in cloud formations are manifold. In the lower regions we find the flat, spreading mobility of warm air, and in the higher regions concentrated cold processes which shape a hard, defined end-product in the formation of ice, but then, this ice formation is torn from its static state by intensive movement. Additionally the polarization is in opposition to the environment; in the cloud's high altitude is darkness and the condensation of matter, where otherwise light shines and matter is dissolved; at the lower altitudes is the upward-striving lightness of a dynamic warmth where usually the weight of horizontal forces predominate.

The thunder-cloud has disengaged itself from the environment and has become, by and large, an independent structure with dramatic polarized processes. Thus it has entered into a close relationship with all living forms and has taken on essential characteristics of these forms. The thunder-cloud assimilates the electric forces, stores them and directs them to powerful electrical polarization from its previous polarization. Here, too, it stands in opposition to its balanced, unpolarized element of air. With the birth of a terrestrial organism in the 'super-terrestrial' region of the higher layers of air, the drama of the thunderstorm begins.

The arising thunder-cloud is, from the beginning, in an electric field between the earth's surface and the upper atmosphere, the ionosphere. The layers of air in betweeen form an insulation-sphere wherein the thunder-cloud grows. The pure air, as an insulating medium, shields living things from the electric currents. However, natural radioactivity and cosmic radiation (as well as pollution) cause a decrease in the air's isolating capacity. This leads to continual electric currents, flowing with a strength of around 1 500 amperes, bridging the potential difference between the ionosphere and the earth's surface of at least 250 000 volts and reducing the electric charge. The potential increases with altitude, so that a person at sea-level is in a quite different electrical field from one standing on a mountaintop where there is a much higher potential. This potential difference is about 100 volts per metre (30 V per foot). Thus a standing person is under a charge of 150 to 200 volts between head and feet, while when he is lying down this potential difference is not there. The strength of the flowing current is, in this case, spread out thinly through space. It is into this electric field that the thunder-cloud grows. Radar measurements have shown conclusively that lightning flashes from the cloud only when the temperature reaches freezing point, that is when the formation of ice commences at an altitude of several kilometres and where, at the same time, the electric potential reaches a high value. The ice-forming stage in the cumulo-nimbus thunder-cloud is thus at the same time the beginning of a new process: the generation of lightning.

The initial charging of the cloud must arise in that sequence of events which occurs between the thunder-cloud's field of ice crystals and the surroundings. Here, due to the high potential, electric forces are active. Following the initial charge thermal, mechanical and electro-dynamic processes are produced in the thunder-cloud, all of which quickly lead to a further charging of the cloud. The high charge and strong current necessary for the lightning thus arises. From an electro-physical point of view, the thunder-cloud is compensating for the continual loss of insulation in the atmosphere and the consequent lowering of the charge between the upper atmosphere and the earth. In the earth's atmosphere cloud masses the size of countries and continents build up highly charged regions which continually restore the potential difference, and discharge daily the superfluous charge in millions of lightning flashes. In this way, clouds and thunder-clouds continually re-establish an archetypal condition.

This archetypal condition reveals itself as an outer phenomenon in the electric charge of the potential difference which expresses the presence of powerful antitheses between the solid earth and the material-dissolving upper atmosphere. The antitheses encounter one another most strongly in the flowering or crystal-process of the thunder-clouds, leading to high charges in the cloud-organism whose surplus electric charge is then released through lightning. When this electric field is looked at not only from the point of view of its external appearance but also from a spiritual aspect, then we find a polarity already considered in the previous chapter. The earthly-mineral world leads, with the help of gravity, to solidification and concentration, finally to the formation of matter; the etheric forces lead through the surrounding activity of the stars to expansion and disintegration, finally to the formation of a vacuum. Without this duality of etheric world and the realm of matter, no organic forms would have arisen on earth. The apple growing on the tree needs material processes which entail gravity, and at the same time the forces of expansion which counteract matter and gravity. The area of tension between the earthly and the etheric world is the earth's actual living space. This tension, however, has a built-in tendency to disintegrate; the disintegration is an expression of ageing or of other circumstances such as pollution or destruction of the atmosphere. The outer expression of the disintegration of etheric light-forces is the phenomenon of the electric potential difference.

Through the forming and subsiding of clouds, above all in the growth of the thunder-clouds, the life-tension field between earth and sky is continually built up and renewed, and thus works against the disintegration of the fertile and necessary state of the electrical potential. The thunder-cloud's measurably increased electric charge is a consequence forced into physical perceptibility of the re-established physical etheric charge of the original polar condition.

At the same time, the lightning arises as an expression of this charge's excess. What the thunder cloud demonstrates in an extreme manner is enacted in every cloud in a milder form. This is revealed by the so called 'bolt from the blue', where only a light cloud-formation can give rise to lightning. An invisible lightning process accompanies the formation of every cloud. Visible lightning is the material product of a prolonged etheric preparation within the cloud's formation. The cloud is the heart of the etheric circulation between the earth's surface and the sky.

A phenomenological consideration of lightning shows how it is projected into our present world from a far distant past. Actually, lightning shows no gradual coming into being but is suddenly there; it bursts forth out of a pent-up, invisible charge in a place that cannot be determined in advance. Light and darkness have no influence on its generation; it comes out of a region where the womb of darkness reigns supreme. Even the commencement of lightning reveals how it appears to come out of a timeless, spaceless world. The thunder-cloud's vertical build-up and the polarization of the whole structure gives the lightning its basic direction — from above downward. The charging up of the cloud and its discharge in lightning runs vertically. However, lightning is soon torn loose from this initial direction. Photographs show how lightning, bit by bit, seeks ever new and unsurmised paths through the air. The lightning's impulse begins ever anew, glows for a stretch through the air, then seeks out a new direction according to the air's particular constitution. Despite this, everything happens in a 'flash of lightning.' In this path-searching process, too, there is neither temporal continuity nor a determinable spatial direction. The thousands of lightning streaks during a thunderstorm show that they have no spatial orientation; the display is chaotic. Lightning is alien in our world.

From the beginning, it grips the air's terrestrial substance and changes it through combustion. Lightning can penetrate as far as mineral matter and even melt the rocks. It can even destroy life. When the total picture of thousands of streaks of lightning is frozen in a photograph, it is as if the air were thronged with glowing roots or an illuminated network of veins. The air appears to be impregnated with fire forces, with creative fire forces which mould the world in its very substance. An important demonstration of this is experienced after a thunderstorm: nature is felt to be born anew; one experiences clearly that it is not only the air cleansed by the rain that gives rise to this new lease of life.

The unbiased soul experiences in the lightning a display of forces which, on the one hand, appear strange and frightening; on the other, familiar and liberating. The impression of strangeness arises against the background of a nature surrounding man in conciliation and harmony. The lightning seems to destroy this harmony. When lightning is seen as a consequence of a needful conciliation the impression of strangeness and fear disappears. Furthermore, it is experienced as kindred when we perceive that we bear within ourselves forces similar to those of the lightning: those of will-power and anger. An uncontrolled display of will-power is shown most clearly in anger which also starts up like a flash of lightning and then expresses itself indiscriminately. However, it can also reveal itself as an expression of will aimed at legitimate conciliation. Then anger acts as a liberation when by its means a harmony of spirit is re-established. Thus the lightning's activity is experienced as a liberation in a circumscribed world by appearing as a manifestation of a hidden yet conciliatory divine will.

Seen as a totality lightning's display has a definite pattern. The spatial distribution stretches around the earth fairly evenly on both sides of the equator to latitudes 20° north and south. In this region lightning occurs for about a hundred to a hundred and eighty days in the year, which means that at certain seasons it happens daily. In this region there are, at the same time, over eight million flashes of lightning daily. This tropical storm belt extends in Australasia from Bombay in the north, through Indo-China, Indonesia, Borneo, Melanesia, to the north and east coast of Australia. There is an area of concentration over Java where there are more than 220 days with thunderstorms in a year. In Africa the belt is mainly present between Madagascar and Natal, and on the west coast in the Gulf of Guinea. In America, the northern part of the belt is somewhat displaced northwards, covering the Caribbean Sea from the north coast of Venezuela, through Central America to southern California, Texas, Louisiana, and Florida. There is an area of concentration around Panama. South America is less affected by the belt, which shows itself in Central Brazil and the coast from Rio de Janiero to Buenos Aires. Latitudes 20° to 30° north and south are transitional regions in which the thunderstorm belt gives way to other forces.

In these regions of the earth, with their inhabited areas, the beginning of the earth's actual development can be seen (Gondwanaland-Lemuria-Paradise) as well as the origin of important human epochs up to the historically ascertainable entry of the Indo-Germanic peoples into India. These old races, cultures and inter-related peoples were an expression of the nature-forces surrounding them. In this particular case, one can speak of an old humanity which stood under the direct influence of the will of a nature still united with God. Its distinctive mark was the lightning which expressed the divine will. This distant epoch of the earth and humanity could be designated the *lightning-era*, whereby it remains an open question as to whether or not lightning at this early time

Plate 19. The red upper part of this aurora curtain arises through the emission of oxygen at heights up to 400 km (250 miles). (Photograph taken by Rüdiger Gerndt in February 1981 in the Esrange Mountains, northern Sweden.)

Plate 20. The auroral corona gathers itself together dramatically like a cloud centre. Its midpoint looks towards the north, below the constellation Cassiopeia. With the bright star in the lower middle of the picture, above the tree-tops, the constellation of Andromeda begins. The constellations are to be seen in these positions only in the extreme north; further south at the same time they are below the horizon. After the formation of a corona, the aurora in northern Europe usually fades away.

120

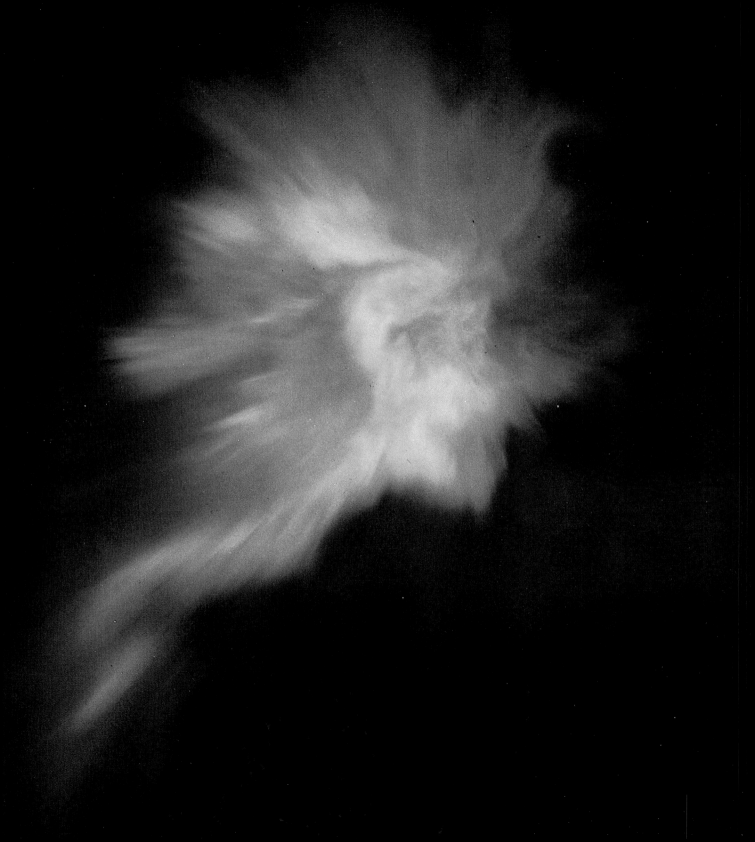

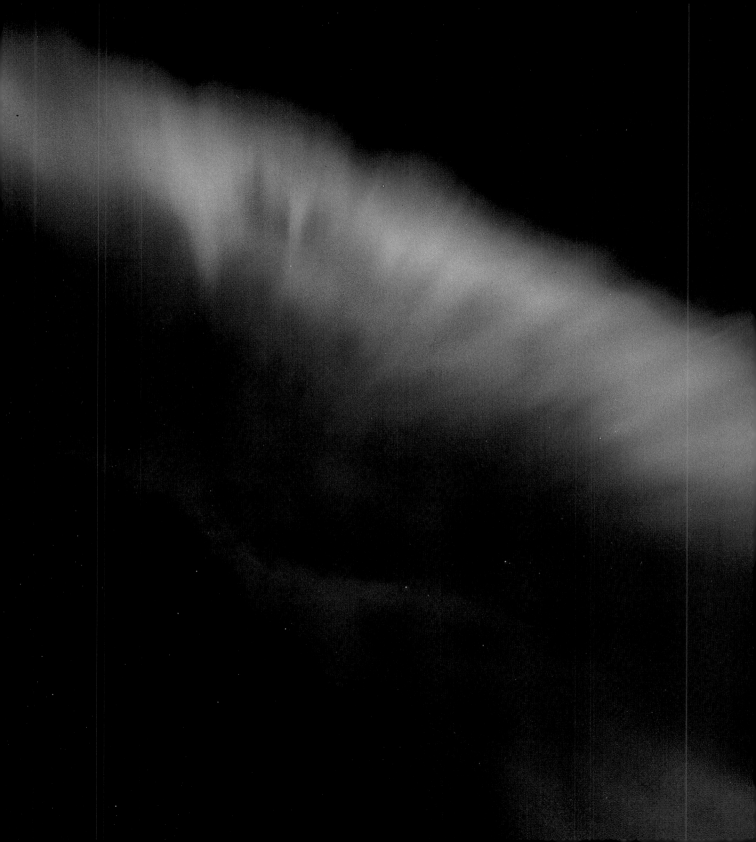

had the same physical character as it does at present. Remnants of this epoch were preserved by the Etruscans, who still possessed a comprehensive teaching on lightning from which they attempted to forecast the future. Insofar as this old epoch of humanity stood predominantly, by way of nature-forces, under the guidance of divine powers, it could be termed humanity under the Father God.

With regard to the reality of the Father God forces, one is faced with hierarchical beings which display the highest powers in the equalization of spirit and matter: the spirits of harmony. They have long been called 'Cherubim' in the Old Testament. Even today we see in the display of lightning activities of these Cherubim. Characteristically, the epoch of the old earth and old humanity under the Father God came to an end through these same powers of the thunderstorm in the clouds and the lightning. It was the Atlantis catastrophe, known as the Flood, that brought this evolutionary period to its close.

Within the earth's thunderstorm belt, the storms accumulate during the hours following the midday heat, that is during the early afternoon. During the course of the year, in the temperate regions where the four seasons appear, thunderstorms gather at the sun's highest, at midsummer and thereafter. In certain tropical regions, thunderstorms always take place at a precise time, with an almost mechanical rhythm. The rise and spread of the lightning occurs here during the sun's powerful radiation of light and heat, darkened and cooled only by the extensive storm-clouds. The regular activity of thunderstorms in this tropical zone at that time of day, when the sun has a burning effect on the earth, gives an extensive and effective protection against the sun to the processes in the earth's crust. Here, in the thunderstorm's shadow and the lightning's light, tropical life can develop.

Plate 21. Like a far-stretching wreath in the sky this auroral corona embraces the constellation of the Great Bear, (the four stars can be seen in the bottom left with the three 'tail' stars to the right). The last of the 'tail' stars, Benetnash shines through the rim of the radiant blue wreath. The 'rays' are curved curtains, stretching up for many hundreds of kilometres and emitting from the celestial north pole below and to the left.

Plate 22. Like a mighty wing this part of an auroral corona stretches across the sky. The centre of the 'rays' of this wing-like wreath is in the north. Such a majestic appearance of an auroral corona is seldom seen.

During these midday hours, human beings are, for a number of reasons, faced with a 'crisis' due above all to the circumstances of the forces-sphere's furthest extension from the earth, described in the preceding chapter. At that time (about 2 to 3 pm), when human consciousness threatens to lose itself in the forces-sphere which is disappearing into higher altitudes, storms become active, with the rousing forces of the lightning. They offer human beings an exhilarating compensation for the deadening forces of midday.

In contrast to the moving drama of the thunderstorm the soothing rainbow in the sky appears like an enchanted vision. A bridge of colour stands lightly on the earth and arches weightlessly across the sky. The radiance of its seven colours shines as though illuminated both from within and from without; the colours blend into one another. The emerging rainbow resembles more a vision than an externally objective perception; its phenomenology reveals the unique significance of this manifestation for humanity since the new beginning after the Flood.

The rainbow is a child of the sunlight and the watery terrestrial atmosphere. Opposite the sun, it follows its course through the day and the seasons. The centre of the rainbow is, apart from rare exceptions, hidden below the horizon, at the 'anti-solar point'. The sun stands exactly opposite, as far *above* the horizon as the rainbow's midpoint lies *below* it. In between lies that part of the earth's surface which hinders the sun's rays from shining directly into the rainbow's middle. The rainbow's complete colour circle is like a colour echo of the sunlight spread out in front of the sun.

In sequence of time, the rainbow follows the thunderstorm in the late afternoon. In temperate northern latitudes at this time, the sun is in the southwest; the rainbow appears opposite, in the northeast. In summer, when the sun is high in the sky, the rainbow is low. As the sun sinks, the rainbow rises until, shortly before sunset, it reaches its most impressive altitude, about 42°, almost half-way to the zenith. As the sun sets, the sharply curved band of colour also fades and disappears. Following a new sunrise in the northeast, the rainbow again appears high in the sky in the southwest; then in the early morning hours it moves across the sky, always opposite the sun, descending westwards. When, in the morning, the sun has reached the corresponding highest point attained by the rainbow in the southeast, about 42°, then the rainbow sinks below the horizon in the northwest. During the hours of midday, when lightning may occur, the rainbow is unable to appear; the sun stands too high for it. Only during the afternoon does the rainbow again rise above the northeastern horizon.

The rainbow's predominant time is not during summer but during the periods when day and night are equal, corresponding to the late afternoon in the course of the day. At about latitude 48° (Paris, Munich, Vienna, Volgograd in Europe; Newfoundland, Vancouver in America, Stewart Island in New Zealand) the midday sun stands, during these periods, at an altitude of about 42°; the rainbow could proceed on its course continually from west to east during the day. During the midday hours, it would sink below the horizon. As the days get longer and the sun rises higher the rainbow sinks below the horizon exactly in the north (south in the southern hemisphere) and remains even longer hidden there during the midday hours until at the summer solstice it is hidden longest.

The rainbow was set up for the newly emerging humanity after the Flood as the sign of a new start. It was the expression of a contract between God and man (Gen.9). In re-orientating themselves, human beings, living in natural surroundings, looked to the rainbow in order to proceed correctly on their way. Earlier peoples had looked up to the planetary gods, above all to the sun-god. Later, people looked up to the solar planet itself, and above all to its rising. With the rainbow's appearance, a particular group of human beings began to look westward to the rainbow, standing in the morning high in the sky and then sinking down. If one considers this new beginning in India, after the Flood, one sees that in looking westward this particular portion of humanity developed an orientation of the will towards the great cultural evolution that was to follow from east to west. To this was added the image of the rainbow descending in the morning. It could point to the earth's penetrating colour-forces in human sense-perception. The being of the colours was to be incarnated.

With this future outlook, the rainbow epoch began. The evolutionary goals were far distant; the human spirit was not at once disposed to be incarnated in this fashion. A man would rather remain with the old planetary gods, or he might seek to leave the earth to return to the spiritual world, later Nirvana, or dissolve himself.

The rainbow has an effect which, compared to lightning, is completely unexpected and novel; the resting bridge of colour allows full freedom. It is not connected to any expression of will, nor does it present any movement that compels the observer to decide in favour of any particular aspect of experience. The rainbow allows human beings the time and possibility to have a restful counterpart. Thus, the phenomenon speaks to the human soul in such a way as to evoke astonishment and admiration. These stirrings of the soul are the beginnings of thinking and love. They could not arise in conjunction with the lightning. It is when he first sees the spectrum colours in terrestrial phenomena that man begins to develop a soul-filled thought-life. However, the great difficulty in this development lies in the fact that no outside stimulus urges the human being to this active thinking. Faced with the colour spectrum, man must develop the thoughts out of his own initiative and in full freedom. In this respect, the rainbow can inspire and motivate him to take up this thinking activity.

This sphere of freedom present in the rainbow was, for post-diluvian human beings, still an aim hidden in the future. Nevertheless, human evolution moved towards this goal as the general rainbow times came more and more into the foreground during the course of the day and year. The human being incarnated in the morning hours; he neither devoted himself to the sun's periodical powers alone, nor did he remain in the dream region of a spiritual world entered at night, but carried these with wakefulness and labour into the earthly world. In the evening, the results of the day's work were assimilated in the soul and the soul's earthly yield was borne into the night's spiritual world. Among the Israelites, the new day even began its activity at the time of transition from afternoon to evening when at sunset a multiplicity of colours appeared in the sky.

The old Indian culture was still, partly, a repetition of humanity's lightning epoch; here, ever and again, man threatened to fall back into connnection with the old nature-powers. However, the embryo for a new human development had been laid in a region which, for humanity, was unequivocally within a new zone of the earth.

Noah, also called Manu, inaugurated this new beginning of humanity beside the Gobi desert in the Tarim basin through which latitude 40° runs. Here, the rainbow forces appeared in full. This latitude also runs through the middle of Greece. Only when the progress of humanity reached the Persian culture did the rainbow's forces begin to display themselves in full. Man looked upward to the sun, but he really sought the sun's aura, that is, the sun's coloured bow. He called it Ahura Mazda.

7. LIGHTNING, RAINBOW, AURORA

Since the perception of these peoples was also directed towards the colour-aura, then culture developed earthwards. Man began to understand the earth and, in a deeper sense, to make it fertile. Persia lies between latitudes 25° and 40°. In the life of the old Israelite peoples, the transition from the lightning to the rainbow forces was repeated in an impressive way within a spiritual-religious development. Still under the influence of lightning and thunder, Moses received on Mount Sinai or Horeb the will-imbued future aim of humanity, which then became the Mosaic Law of the ten commandments (Exod.20). However, a few centuries later, the prophet Elijah could no longer find these forces in lightning and thunder. He found them in a cave — on the same mountain — following storm, earthquake and fire, in the 'still, small voice' in which the Lord God appeared. No rainbow is spoken of here; it cannot appear in a cave; outside there was no rain, Elijah prevented it. However, the 'still, small voice' is the expression of the same elementary condition as can be experienced in facing the rainbow. After the storm, there is the 'quiet calm' in which the rainbow appears. Elijah's mighty fire-spirit achieved the inner rainbow experience.

The Greek world was then the genuine rainbow-culture of humanity. Philosophy awoke out of the wonder for colourful phenomena, and love of the earth arose from admiration of the sense-world. One gets a complete picture of the Greek rainbow culture only when, to the abstract images of colourless white pillars and other temple remains, one adds the intensive colour with which these Hellenic buildings were painted. It was a joyful marriage with the colour spectrum.

However, the rainbow should not be understood only in relation to the sense-world, as in the case of the Greeks; independently of this, it should be attained in the individual human being as the result of his soul's union with the earth. This development had its beginning with Christ's resurrection. When the painter Mathis Grünewald (c. 1460–1528) represented, in the Isenheimer altar picture, the resurrected Christ rising out of the earth's heaviness in the darkness of night, he surrounded him with a radiantly powerful colour-aura out of which all the soul-power of the resurrection speaks to the spectator. The rainbow's original promise had here attained its goal.

The greatest challenge which the rainbow presented to man was the question of its genesis. This question had historical dimensions. As a question in the sense of present-day thinking, it could be posed only in the rising age of natural science. At the beginning of the eighteenth century, Sir Isaac Newton (1642–1727) came up with the first answer; sunlight (which he thought of in material terms), the sun's ray, was split up into the colours of the spectrum when it penetrated a medium. His proof of this was to look through a glass prism; the rainbow was thought to arise, analogically, in the same manner. Modern optics evolved out of this conception; light was understood in its physical relationship and its laws were investigated.

When, many years later, Goethe learnt of these thoughts and experiments, he decided to test them for himself. Among other things, he borrowed a prism, but for a long time left it lying unused. When the time arrived for him to return it to its owner, he darkened his room and directed his eye through the prism. He saw something completely different from what he expected from Newton's description; he observed how the colour spectrum appeared only where the edge of the light coincided with a dark edge. Goethe realized that the coloured spectrum appeared only where light and darkness act together. With this observation a chasm opened between two conceptions of the nature of light and colour; it actually arose over the nature of the rainbow's colour spectrum.

Following this, Goethe tried indefatigably to show that Newton's conception was an abstract theory because in the essential content of the experience the darkness had not been taken into account; for him, Newton's theory did not divulge the nature of light and colour. The universal practicality of Newton's interpretation in optics and technology appeared to contradict Goethe's conception. Thus, Goethe's colour theory was almost completely ignored and forgotten — the victory seemed to go to Newton. With the rise of Anthroposophy in the twentieth century through Rudolf Steiner, Goethe's conception was taken up again, and methodically developed.

The rainbow's appearance after the Flood was not only a revelation of beauty on the part of nature. It was the expression of a far-reaching change in the nature of the earth. Before the Flood, parts of the earth's atmosphere were filled with fog, thicker than fog is today. This dense atmosphere was, at the same time, the expression of a lively, labile terrestrial nature containing a surplus of life-activities which, again, were closely connected with human life. The earth was still a visibly living being. Through this entwinement of terrestrial nature and human life, the trespasses of mankind called forth the Flood.

After the destruction, the divine world revealed the manner in which the earth had become different: 'While the earth remains, seed-time and harvest, cold and heat, summer and winter, day and night, shall not cease' (Gen.8:22).

> I will remember my covenant which is between me and you and every living creature of all flesh; and the waters shall never again become a flood to destroy all flesh. When the bow is in the clouds, I will look upon it and remember the everlasting covenant between God and every living creature of all flesh that is upon the earth. (Gen.9:15f).

However comforting these words were, and are, for humanity, they conceal a tremendous assertion: the earth had entered a phase of repetition of identity. The existence of life is assured, but at the cost of genuine, immediate unpredictable life. From this time on, the earth could be comprehended as a dead and computable body. In the repetitiveness, nothing new would be revealed. The rainbow was also an expression of this. The colours, which still fill the atmosphere with flowing movement today, are tied down to a fixed order in the rainbow. This is actually an alien phenomenon for the lively, mobile atmosphere. The living weaving of colours enters here into the predictability of a dead situation. From this time on, light is revealed through the colours in a dual manner: as life it is incalculable and difficult to grasp — as death, calculable and understandable. Both were still to be found in the rainbow; but the living content remained, to begin with, hidden in the external order. Thus the scientific age approached the obvious dead aspect of the phenomena. Newton investigated the calculable and deadness in light; it was immediately susceptible to technical-mechanical treatment. Goethe took the hard way; he tried to grasp the living incommensurable; the incomprehensible was to be made the subject of contemplation. It was difficult to find followers along this way. The gap between both conceptions will be closed through further living understanding of the rainbow's spectrum itself.

The rainbow arises in the medium of the atmosphere's moisture. This moisture consists of an overwhelming number of drops ranging from microscopic droplets to raindrops of almost centimetre size. The droplet forms the embryo of all atmospheric phenomena in the sky. When someone goes through a dew-laden meadow or wood, he is immediately in this world of droplets. The drops, full of colour and light, shine and sparkle with unceasing variation. Each drop mirrors and refracts the landscape of the whole environment; it does what the earth's watery atmosphere also does as a whole: it reflects, disperses and deflects the sunlight. In contemplating the rainbow, man experiences what is happening in the water droplet's interior. In order to make the outer events clear, it is first necessary to be abstract and speak of the sun's rays. Such a ray is a constructed concept which is necessary to make external facts geometrically conceptual and measurable. The sun's rays that strike the droplet exactly in the middle and penetrate it are reflected on the opposite concave inner side of the droplet and return in the same direction. The bright flash as of a diamond within the dewdrop signifies that the human eye has caught sight of these reflected rays and was thereby placed in the axis of sun to droplet. The other rays falling on the droplet are firstly refracted (bent inwards) by the droplet's curved surface, and in different directions according to the point of impact on the droplet's curvature. Around the edges the rays cannot penetrate the droplet. All the rays which have entered are secondly reflected inside the droplet and are very much dispersed, all at different angles. The third deflection takes place as they emerge from the droplet where they are again refracted. The result is an emerging angle of 42° to the sun's rays falling centrally into the middle of the droplet.

As the exit from the droplet takes place everywhere on the hemisphere turned towards the sun, there arises in the surroundings a projected colour cone of 42°, showing the colour spectrum. The imbibed light of the sun and the imbibed darkness of the sun's surroundings are layered in the droplet through reflection and refraction so that, in re-emerging, the colour spectrum has arisen. It is the same procedure as in the prism but on account of the droplet's curvature there arises a colour cone instead of a band.

In the larger, secondary rainbow, light and darkness come forth only after a second reflection inside the droplet so that a larger angle of emergence (51°) gives rise to the colour spectrum. On account of the dual refraction-reflection, the light's penetration is weakened and so the secondary rainbow appears more faintly. The rainbow in the landscape presupposes a space filled with a veil of water droplets. In each droplet the same thing occurs as in the dewdrop: the colour cone is rayed out to the sun. In theory, every moisture-saturated space is suffused with a flood of unlimited colour. If the observer directs his gaze to the 'invisible' colour flows, his eye will become the crystallizing point for a *single* colour cone belonging to his viewpoint. The human eye behaves like the droplet of water; perceptual space is also a cone. Where this cone of vision penetrates colour-permeated space and meets with a selection of the radiating colours, there arises in the droplet the necessary projection surface on which the visual colour band can arise in space. Each individual drop of water gives necessary individual colour for the emergence of the whole bow, that is, the eye sees just this colour, and indeed different colours at different altitudes in the bow.

In order that the rainbow may appear, one must stand with the sun at one's back and look into the space where the sun produces the inundation of colour. This colour inundation surrounds a human being as a possibility; a particular coloured bow appears to his sight as one of innumerable possibilities arising from a particular perspective. The colour circle comes into being; its upper portion appears as a rainbow. The forces of light and darkness penetrate to human beings through these colours: 'When the bow is in the clouds, I will look upon it and remember . . . every living creature'. God, still active in atmospheric nature, could look upon human beings when the rainbow appeared.

The rainbow does not enter fully into the earthly world; it remains partly in a supersensory realm. Regarded physically, the bow is only an optical phenomenon without any matter or energy; it really exists only for human beings and, on closer scrutiny, only for human beings individually — in this it expresses its most profound significance: its relationship to the human 'I'. Every human being sees his own rainbow; even a neighbour, standing close beside his, sees a different rainbow. Looked at in this way, there is no objective rainbow; one and the same bow cannot be seen or photographed from two sides. This points to a far-reaching fact of human perception; each human being stands in his own perceptual spatial dimension which possesses an individual character. To begin with, his 'I' is hidden in this spatial dimension. In the activity of perceiving and thinking which a human being develops, his 'I' begins to appear. This activity has the character of the rainbow. The coloured bow makes it especially apparent how decisively the position of the human being in space, and the human being himself, contributes to the production of his perceptions.

This can be extended to apply to all perceptions; from the point of view of outer circumstances, they are always of an individual 'I', at least potentially. If to the rainbow percept is added the optically living event which, with the help of the human eye, conjures up a two-dimensional picture, then this picture-process will resemble the summoning up of a concept which, incidentally, also appears only in two-dimensional space. Here, perceiving and conceiving approach one another. For this reason arises the almost visionary and somewhat unreal perception of the rainbow colour-spectrum. This perception and the associated experience is only appropriated by the individual. It remains subjective and obscure as long as the individual only experiences it for himself. An objective truth arises here only when the human being overcomes his individual experience and broadens it in such a way that he crosses the threshold to the perception and experience of his fellow beings. To attain this he must put himself through his thinking, experiencing and willing in the place of his fellow beings.

This usually occasions great difficulty and is really possible only when an excess of power is developed which is not naturally present. It may be regarded as higher 'I'-force because it attempts to embrace the individual and separated human 'I's. In this situation, the image of the higher human being arises, the genuine human being, that proceeds out of overcoming the basically subjective 'I'. This higher 'I' can also be called the 'Son of Man', in as much as it proceeds as 'Son' out of the working together of individuals. It is with this 'I' of the Son of Man that the objective truth sought after by human beings then also appears.

When, after the Flood, the rainbow was placed before man as an image of the covenant between God and the human world, man received, concealed within himself, the image of this future being of the Son of Man. The sevenfold colours were, at the same time, a phenomenon that came out of the creation of the earth. For the creator God, who is described in Genesis, was experienced — as already mentioned — as a divinity of multiplicity, namely in a sevenfold form. The traces within the work of creation of the Elohim are to be found in the many sevenfold groupings which penetrate the structure of our world: the seven potentially visible rainbows and aurora arcs, the classical seven planets, the seven weekdays, the seven notes of the scale and, finally, the sevenfold human being. In every choir of sevenfoldness the image of the Son of Man as the actual creator-spirit, Christ, the Logos, was concealed; his appearance was still veiled in the sevenfold radiating colours of the rainbow.

The human situation existing under the sign of the rainbow could be called the Son Humanity. These people had settled in a region of the earth where the rainbow-revelation begins to replace the lightning's realm of forces. This region of the earth stretches, in the

Northern and Southern hemispheres north and south of latitude 30° respectively. In the northern hemisphere, latitude 30° runs south of Lahore in Pakistan, through southern Iran directly across the estuary of the rivers Euphrates and Tigris, (Abraham's home town, Ur of the Chaldees, lies a little to the north). It passes about 2° south of Jerusalem, cuts through Cairo in Egypt and then crosses the Mediterranean coast of North Africa. In North America it continues through New Orleans and Houston and runs about 4° south of Los Angeles to cross the North Pacific basin and graze the southern tip of Japan. In China, latitude 30° passes south of Shanghai and through the region of the Yangtze River. Lhasa in Tibet lies on this latitude, which then runs over the Himalayas again to Persia.

Correspondingly, in the Southern hemisphere, latitude 30° crosses over South Africa about level with Durban; in South America, Porto Alegre in Southern Brazil lies in its path, which continues to the coast of Chile 3° north of Valparaiso, then crosses the South Pacific basin 5° north of New Zealand to run along a line in the north of New South Wales through the Great Victoria Desert and 2° north of Perth. A glance at this circumscribed region on the earth with its human circumstances makes it perfectly clear what an overwhelming significance the rainbow-region has.

Lightning and rainbows are for the most part well known to humanity. On the other hand, it is characteristic of the aurora that, up to now, it has remained largely concealed from humanity. Since the full phenomenon entered into humanity's perception and dawning conceptuality only in the twentieth century, it disclosed itself as something for the future. The comprehensive phenomenon of the aurora can still not be fully understood today. That is still a task for the future.

To begin with, the isolated phenomena of the aurora are fragmentary, yet are present in an almost unsurveyable abundance. Its total form is difficult to apprehend. However, in Europe, at least, a rhythmical structure is discernible; it begins with the arc. Surprisingly, it replaces the rainbow spatially-temporally in the same way as the rainbow does the lightning. As previously mentioned, in spring the rainbow sets at midday in the north and towards summer remains hidden longer. Correspondingly, at midday, as winter draws on, (with its low-lying sun visible much less often than in summer) the rainbow fades and disappears through unfavourable weather conditions. In the same direction of the heavens the auroral arcs appear in the earth's more northern latitude. In this region of the earth, the first phase of the auroral phenomenon, the auroral arcs, replace the sinking or disappearing rainbows.

The rainbow appears, above all, in the hours of the late afternoon; the auroral display follows on immediately and begins in the early evening. Further rhythmical activity forms the auroral arc, which is still at rest, and generates the oscillating band of the aurora. Movement arises; it is the central and most characteristic aspect of the following auroral display, which rises to the most intensive mobility. The filling of the heavens begins with the draperies and curtains and culminates in the corona. The fading signifies disintegration. Form creation and disintegration determine the aurora's course in the sky. The colours present in the static rainbow are liberated in the auroral display. They are merged in an extensive spatial-planetary consistency. In contrast to lightning and rainbow, the extent of the phenomenon is immensely enlarged; neither lightning nor rainbow is visible from outer space, but the aurora is. Lightning and rainbow can be seen from localities on the earth as self-contained phenomena. The entire spatial phenomenon of the aurora can be grasped only with difficulty through many observations over great parts of the earth and only in the present day can it be photographed by satellite from outer space. The general view thus attained shows a vast structure, the oval, like a flower, directed towards the cosmos.

The earth's aurora, therefore, cannot be perceived in its entirety by any isolated observer. In the process of comprehending the aurora, human consciousness would first have to extend into the whole context of the earth and then into that of the planets. The cause of the rainbow is the sunlight weaving in the terrestrial realm; that of the aurora is concealed in invisible occurrences in the immensely extended terrestrial magnetosphere under the influence of the sun and its hollowing-out processes. In concerning himself with this sphere, the human being is entering a cosmic realm and investigating a phenomenon that must be termed 'wind' in justifiable comparison with terrestrial wind. Lightning corresponds to a realm that is not directly connected with the sun or the light; it appears

Plate 23. In this photograph sunlight and aurora appear together. The sun follows its course below the horizon and casts up delicate colours over the earth. In the heights auroral bands have formed like clouds of a kind. Thus the aurora shining on its own account, can also be lit by the sun.

by day and by night quite independently of the light. The rainbow arises only in and through sunlight. The aurora, on the other hand, is also independent of light and darkness, but it is, at the same time, a *direct* expression of terrestrial and solar activity and their substances. In lightning, the energies are discharged in eruption; they are quite unregulated. The rainbow shows no such energies. During an auroral display, powerful energies are released gradually in a perceptibly regulated, structured and mobile procedure.

The phenomena of lightning, rainbow and aurora take hold of the earth's rhythmical structures and spatial dimensions step by step. In so doing they disclose an evolution which develops in three phases. The lightning's activity has its culmination by day, in the midday hours; in the course of the year it is in summer. Here, there is little rhythmic activity; time rests, as it were, and is still attached to space; movement of the sun is hardly taken into account. The rainbow's times during morning and afternoon, in spring and in autumn, show the beginnings of a rhythmical development. Here, in time, one state begins to slide over into the other; the morning into midday and the afternoon into the evening. As an expression of a terrestrial natural law, the static rainbow is fitted into this river of time but nevertheless rises and sinks with the sun's movement. The rhythm in the stream of time actually arises with the change from darkness to light and vice versa; that is, with the alternation of day and night, with the seasonal changes in temperate zones and the particularly intensive changes in northernmost latitudes, where summer and winter are as day to night. The aurora is to be found in this region, beginning in the evening, with the most intensive display until midnight. It can often remain until morning. In the polar regions themselves, it is replaced by the daytime aurora already described. When, here, the aurora shows a rhythmical structure which covers the whole day, it is demonstrating its correspondence with the eleven-year solar rhythm as an extension into cosmic rhythms. In the auroral rhythm there is a mobility which does not

Plate 24. *When the deployment of the aurora has passed its highest point — often with the formation of a corona — a quiet period sets in. Individual patches of light and colour, at various places in the sky, call to mind the aurora's wide-spreading curtains. These coloured clouds can linger quietly in the sky for several hours. In the photograph they are reflected together with the stars, in a quiet expanse of water.*

133

really exist in the lightning. Lightning is an impulse which functions by shooting or striking. The lightning always runs on a definite course, moving in short straight spasms. The rainbow itself has no movement; it weaves within itself. Only in ascending and descending does the rainbow reflect the sun's movement. It is only in the aurora's activity that real movement takes place, going over into an intensive widespread dynamism.

In a spatial context, lightning appears as a one-dimensional event, as a jagged structure that seeks its course as a path of light; it displays itself always only in the first dimension, rapidly tearing itself loose from any orientation in space, wanting to establish a situation on the border of the first dimension's spacelessness. The rainbow is quite different. It fits unequivocally into terrestrial space. But it lacks the third dimension; in its purely optical appearance it presents only a two-dimensional image related to a projection. The aurora embraces the whole of space. In its bowl-like oval, it forms an archetypal image of three-dimensional space.

The final development and conclusion of this trinitarian evolution of the terrestrial-luminous phenomena in the aurora shows the aurora to be an expression of the Spirit. Like the aurora, the Spirit has always been the hidden and unknown in the historical periods of human evolution. Before the Christian era the Spirit could be found only in the secrecy of the world beyond. And since that time it is only slowly penetrating the sphere of human experience. In the same way the aurora shows itself to human beings; it was only in the twentieth century when humanity became a comprehensive and interrelated society that the being of the aurora came fully into appearance. It is an image of the Pentecostal event of earth and humanity and bears essential marks of this event within it. The colours of the aurora burn like flames over the earth similar to the flames above the heads of those human beings who experienced the original Whitsun. It is said of those flames that they sank down upon the human beings. The aurora, too, can be so described, only with reference to the whole earth. In the aurora's background, the solar wind occurs; it is incalculable, and it can on no account, despite all today's prognostic power, be predicted where this plasma wind will conjure up the aurora. It is, in the first place, an extra-terrestrial, physical, natural phenomenon, but reveals itself as a kind of 'solar-meteorological animation'. As the terrestrial wind in the New Testament is experienced as an image of the Spirit, ('a sound from Heaven like the rush of a mighty wind', Acts 2:2), so likewise in a similar way — extended into the earth's environment — the solar wind is an articulated image of a superposed movement of the Spirit, now in its cosmic-terrestrial form.

This event can approach human beings today as a challenge to knowledge. Progressive Christianity will learn to see the earth in conjunction with the Pentecostal event. The aurora's nature is — like the yet unrevealed spirit — of the future. Latitude 60° presents a human threshold to which present culture and civilization have penetrated and where one looks into a future which today raises more questions than answers. Human beings in cultural circumstances north of this latitude, for example in Northern Europe and Alaska, are living under existential conditions which, in terms of consciousness, may be understood by humanity only in the future.

The overall view of lightning, rainbow and aurora shows an archetypal interaction of trinitarian forces in the earth's environment. As long as the lightning is tied to the cumulo-nimbus thunder-clouds which, at rest, are built up from below upwards, then it will penetrate from above downwards, the lightning discharging in a vertical electric field. It thus expresses its being — still tied to the built-up clouds, it unites the upper with the lower; finally, lightning is the union of the starry heights and the terrestrial depths. The human being, standing erect, is placed into this field of tension. He lifts his eyes to the heights as the realm in which the divine forces from the past have been active with the powers of creation. At the same time he is aware of the depths as the sustaining Father-ground of being. In looking at the lightning, he experiences the archaic source of the forces which, today, still unite the heights with the depths. They are the Father-forces. Fear of the lightning can turn into reverence for being. Anger in the human being, as the soul's expression of these Father-forces, can develop into conscious will.

The rainbow demonstrates the horizontal forces; in its arch, as a colour bridge, it connects one part of the landscape with another. Together with the shimmer of colours, to be found again everywhere in nature, it points to the earth's surrounding surface. The colours are a revelation of that which appertains to the soul; it is through the rainbow that man unites with the world around him. Thoughts intense with feeling, and love of his surroundings arise. The particular perceptual relationship between human beings and the rainbow leads to the image of the human 'I' that finds true expression in the Son of Man. The colour circle's horizontal bow crosses the vertical stem of the lightning's forces in the heights. An atmospheric terrestrial cross arises.

The environmental forces of the Spirit are fitted into this cross through the activities of the aurora in human consciousness. The aurora appears, in planetary terms, as a rounded structure, as a closed light-circle, which adds the solar motif of resurrection to the cross. However, the resurrection appears, to begin with, in connection with the earth, not directly with the human soul. This puts the human being of the present day in a quandary. Must he first experience the forces of the resurrection as a reality on the planet earth before he himself may receive them? Many things at the present time point in this direction. The aurora reveals further, the connection of earth and human beings with the cosmos. Above all, it poses the question of the future: how will humanity continue to develop towards the 'Aurora-Epoch' in which, on earth, people become conscious of their spiritual relationship to the cosmos. What does this presuppose? Here the understanding of the aurora leads into an apocalyptic future.

In the New Testament, the Revelation to St John (4:2–6) gives a first description of the spiritual-divine world: In the middle, on a throne, surrounded by twenty four elders clad in white garments, the Creator of the universe; a rainbow, that looks like emerald surrounds him. From the throne issue flashes of lightning, and voices and peals of thunder. Before the throne burn seven torches of fire, designated as the seven spirits of God. Later, these spirits will be sent out over the earth by the Lamb, who also stands there. Also before the throne is spread a sea of glass, like crystal.

In the rainbow, which surrounds the centre of this envisioned spiritual world, we see the mineral condition of creation. Through the continued working of Christianity on the earth, the impulse of the resurrection penetrates the whole of existence. The whole of created crystalline creation is thus slowly brought back into the spiritual world. There it receives, in a changed form, a new being. In the rainbow, an image of Christianity can be seen here below; here it is still colourful, pictorial and embryonic with light. In the spiritual world it will be penetrated by those forces which, on earth, most clearly belong to the world of the dead — the mineral forces. They, too, will be led into the resurrection and their eternal forces united with the rainbow's being. Thus the rainbow represents the product of the Christian metamorphosed earth. The centre of the rainbow shines green. Green is the predominant colour of organic terrestrial life, which also in the emerald rainbow receives its duration in another world. Concerning this, basic information is given in the Revelation to St John: the life centralized and gathered together on earth is seen in its new changed form as a mineral-like rainbow.

Lightning issues from the throne itself. On earth, lightning brings mighty forces from on high into earthly existence. In the envisioned spiritual world it is the other way round: the flashes of lightning issue from the centre of the throne; they form there a kind of foundation for the throne. Here, too, as with the rainbow, the spatial relationship is reversed. However, neither do lightning and thunder remain what they are in the realm of earth. As with the rainbow, something seems to be added: the voices. Lightning and thunder are experienced by human beings only as natural phenomena; but one can come to know that human thinking and speaking have their correlation in lightning and thunder. In the spiritual world, the forces of nature and the forces of man, which have fallen apart, are brought together again: with lightning and thunder, voices are blended; the comprehensible word unites with the lightning from the throne and speaks into the environment. The activity of the Cherubim, which is otherwise incomprehensible to human beings, becomes understandable in a supersensory world through the voices.

The aurora is not mentioned in the Apocalypse. Although it was known to a few individuals, it was unknown to humanity in general at the time of St John's receiving the Revelation. One would have expected it to be mentioned at this point, following rainbow and lightning. In fact, immediately following the account of the lightning's activity, a fiery phenomenon is spoken of: the seven burning torches which are called the seven spirits of God. They are, from the oldest time, the seven creative spirits which stand at the beginning in Genesis. As already described, they are called 'Spirits of Form' because they give form to all existence, including the structure and form of the rainbow. These hierarchic spirits have put their signature on the world so firmly that over immense periods of time man could be immersed only in contemplating the created forms. The old Hebrew Sabbath experience was actually the fully active and passive devotion to this created world of forms. For it was humanity's destiny and task to take up this world of forms into itself. In this way, man learnt to think in conformity with the earth.

But gradually a total eclipse crept in; perception of the spiritual world disappeared. What remained was form-perception and formal thinking. It was against this that Christ made his decisive combat. Christ, the hidden lord of the Elohim spirits of creation, was able to reopen the creator-spirits' influence which had been closed, to loosen the form-hardening and to continue the act of creation. A new creation was established. It is no longer primarily a creation of the Elohim. Through Christ's entry into humanity, certain beings that stood closer to man on the hierarchic ladder, the angels, were impulsively moved. The act of creation was opened in a downward direction, and man too was fully united with it. At the same time an opening was made in an upward direction; the creative spirits that revealed themselves through the action of Christianity disclosed the co-operative working of those hierarchical beings who stand immediately behind and over the Elohim. These are the Dynameis, the 'Spirits of Movement'. In the course of western Christian development, it can be clearly seen how these spirits, coming out of the background, work more and more into the world. This is seen first of all, one-sidedly, in the scientific discoveries which concentrated primarily on the movements of the planets. The so-called Copernican revolution was initiated through the discovery of new laws of motion. Motion also took hold of spiritual and religious life; the Renaissance tried to find a new image of man, new continents were discovered and in the Reformation a new religious life was sought for. This change in the Christian confession of faith first received conscious acknowledgement in the twentieth century, when in the Creed of The Christian Community the Father God is spoken of as the being 'who goes before his creatures like a Father'. The experience and concept of a static creator had been overcome.

In the nineteenth and twentieth centuries this impulse towards motion in the fields of science and technology broke all hitherto conceivable bounds. The theory of evolution, for example, replaced the static doctrine of creation. Human thinking overcame stagnation and stands, therefore, before infinite possibilities in good and evil. Regarded spiritually, this means that the spirits of the burning torches standing before God's throne, in the Apocalypse's image of the future, have taken upon themselves, in dynamic fire, the workings of the Dynameis and now ray them out upon humanity, 'sent out into all the earth' (Rev. 5:6). It is as if the Elohim's darkly formed, opaquely created form-structures lit up and became transparent for the rays of fire of the sun-related Dynameis. It is under such influences that the further advance of a new creation is accomplished.

The celestial image of the aurora is an immediate expression of these events. It shines over the earth's polar ice fields, which appear related to the sea of glass in the Apocalypse. The aurora's light and weaving colour is gripped from within; it is displayed quite independently of any created outer forms. At the same time the aurora continually produces new forms; but they gleam and are lit up by a moving, solar-related fire. The revelation of a working of the Exousiai, the Forming Spirits, and of the Dynameis, the fiery-moving Spirits is accomplished in an exalted super-terrestrial harmony. This event is not disturbed by any unassimilated remainder of indissoluble forms. Corresponding to this is the body-free thinking within the human being, where lively-formative concepts arise and vanish in order to penetrate to higher truths. It is the thinking of the future.

After Fridtjof Nansen had stood before the auroral display many times, he realized what these spiritual circumstances implied (1904, 131): 'I have never been able to grasp the fact that this earth will some day be spent and desolate and empty. To what end, in that case, all this beauty, with not a creature to rejoice in it? Now I begin to divine it. *This* is the coming earth "here are beauty and death".' Through this realization, the aurora becomes a unique symbol of our present and future.

8. Theodor Däubler: herald of the northern lights

When, in 1898, the poet Theodor Däubler (1876–1934) began to write his comprehensive epic on the northern lights, the entire phenomenon of the northern auroral oval was still in the twilight phase of its first discovery. Only eighteen to nineteen years had passed since the planetary dimensions of the oval had been recognized in outline by Sophus Tromholt (about 1879). Däubler was born three years earlier. Even for those involved in science, this discovery was long to remain hidden, for it seemed far-reaching and complicated. It has become generally known only in the most recent years through satellite photographs of the auroral oval. Däubler was the first to recognize, astonishingly early, the full range of this discovery. He added to the scientific data a number of conceptions which anticipate the conscious contents of a 'spirit-humanity.' Thus Däubler sees the auroral oval as an expression of a living earth-organism and, at the same time, as the sign of a new knowledge of the pentecostal state of the earth.

In cultural-historical terms, Däubler arranged the northern lights as an inner and outer guiding phenomenon within humanity's great journey from the beginnings of culture in the earth's south-east to the present-day cultures in the north-west. He saw a process corresponding to that of the aurora in the development of spiritual light within the human being. Above all, he recognized this in humanity's moral disposition. This human 'polar light' is connected, in a mysterious way, with the earth's auroral ovals. Thus, in the phenomenon of these ovals Däubler sees the expression of a higher union of the cosmically permeated earthly nature and the striving human spirit. A scientific fact, having no other value, is connected with the evolution of humanity.

Already in the scientific comprehension of the aurora, Däubler was far ahead of his contemporaries. Since they did not know, neither empirically nor theoretically, what Däubler spoke and wrote poetry about with such enthusiasm and intoxication, the most essential portion of his poetry remained incomprehensible and misjudged. His broadening views of the auroral ovals may be regarded as

Figure 21. Theodor Däubler in Greece, 1923.

significant discoveries comparable to those of Goethe's archetypal plant, where the essentials must be drawn out afterwards by an act of will and imagination. However, even without these efforts, Däubler's observations raise questions which, at the present time, are of urgent concern for the future of humanity and the earth.

Thus Theodor Däubler became a human being initiated into the aurora's sign. The auroral initiation brought him knowledge and insights that point towards a distant future; it gave him, at the same time, a literary creative power that, in its breadth, depth and novelty can only be gradually recognized. It is not surprising that in 1923 the cultural philosopher and writer Rudolf Pannwitz (1881–1969) had to say of the poet Däubler's work (Däubler 1956, 879): 'All this is a treasure for the mastering of which life is not long enough, but for which many lives would be well spent . . . [we] must accept the whole of it as it is, as a new virgin forest and a cultivated forested continent'.

When this was said, Däubler was only forty-seven years old; it would also have been pertinent in 1910, for then Däubler, at thirty-four, had already finished his powerful epic, *Das Nordlicht*. This work, with its thirty-three thousand verses, was written partly in Vienna, mostly in Paris. The inspiration for this epic stretches back into Däubler's youth; he had heard of Tommaso Campanella (1568–1639) and his work *City of the Sun* (*La città del sole*), and now wanted to write a similar work under the title, *Impero del Sole*, 'Empire of the Sun'. Later, in Naples where in his early years he always wanted to live, the twenty-two-year-old youth was over-powered by pictures and visions at the foot of Mount Vesuvius. He immediately began making notes for his forthcoming major work, whose title and essential content had changed considerably by contrast with his solar visions of earlier years. It was now called simply *Nordlicht*, 'Northern Lights'.

Between the condensed terrestrial fire of a volcano, where the epic had its beginning, and the veil-curtained weightlessness of the aurora there seemed to yawn a deep abyss. In Däubler's spirit, however, planetary cosmic inspiration and intuitions were inter-woven, not only bridging these contrasts but incorporating them into an evolutionary vision. This vision embraced the path from an archaic sun realm through the dark being of the earth to a new shining planetary state. In the centre of this vision stands the aurora.

In the landscape of his homeland, then Austrian Istria, Däubler had not seen the aurora. Nor had he seen it in Trieste where, in

8. THEODORE DÄUBLER

1876, he was born and grew up. One cannot infer from any expression or account by the later poet that he had ever seen the aurora. All comments and descriptions bear the amazing mark of an intuitive perception that ever and again astonishes one profoundly by the exactness of its nature. During his youth and early manhood, Däubler journeyed often through wide areas of the Mediterranean countries and southern Europe; nowhere is there an indication that he had attempted to see the aurora in northern Europe. In later years, he made some journeys to southern Scandinavia, and to Oslo. The unique characteristic of this incongruity is clearly demonstrated in the fact that Däubler was concerned to express a deeply experienced intuition in its conceptual and imaginative formation and not to depict an external landscaped romance. When one considers that this poetic personality has expressed more about the aurora, both in depth and breadth, than all other poets in the world together and yet had never seen the northern lights, then we are faced with a unique and astonishing fact. It lies in a kind of clairvoyance which led to a direct activity of spirit in Däubler. In 1919 he wrote in Dresden about the origin of this spiritual intuition in the foreword to *Das Nordlicht* (1921, 11ff).

> Once, at a masked ball (I myself wore a mask) I said to myself: Life is not merely a voluntary ascetism or constraint, a duty opposed to the sun in order that we may climb to the highest stars, and the earth is not merely an enemy, at best a vagina and grave. It occurred to me in effect: life demands abundance, the creatures ought to jubilate divinely upwards. I ran out of the ballroom on to the street. I felt happy, the earth concealed within itself yet a great amount of sun which was united with us in opposition to gravity and wanting to return to the sun. Everywhere. Even in the ice. Especially there, at the poles, where the night is deepest, longest, particularly powerful! A shining embrace of sun redeemed from earth and the sun in the sky brings the aurora to the months-long nights at the poles. The earth longs to be a shining star again. My private cosmogony had attained its completion!
>
> This idea of the northern crown would not leave me. I knew quickly that it could, in fact, be desire, joy, happiness, trust within ourselves. For me, the reason for this lay, I saw it clearly, in the earth. Perhaps in a fluid-fiery, still sunlike interior! Light's destination, the gleaming

wreaths round the poles, became for me a symbol of the history of the innermost occurrences. I experienced a northern shining of the soul; what happened there made all creatures of the day dim. The sun eclipsed itself for me. At night, my confidence dawned in a final, mediating sun. The aurora can show us the way to it. It brings us closer to the archetypal light. We are descended from it, we human beings who have determined, weighed and made into our own act all visible suns. In my impulsiveness, I did not shrink back for one moment from entrusting my naïve atheism to a heavenly faith in hierarchies and supernatural spirituality. The leap into the religious was, however, an act of will! Quite childishly, I wanted to embrace all my acquaintances, to see their souls as paths to the North belonging to all peoples. Thus, again, with human beings, as one who would break open the archetypal light, an equal! Often, locked up with myself, I had prayed in secret; now I admitted to myself that I prayed. Through the northern lights, I received the freedom of our race. Every human being, I said to myself, uses it as choice of a vision, each individual can also decide where and when he will be born. We are not mere subjects of a visible sun!

The following, however, remains as the task of humanity — to realize the future of the earth through the northern lights! We proclaim, the earth will shine once more, but the peoples are responsible that this dark star will some day become the brightest of all. Not a transient planet but the field of our holiest mission is from now on our radiant star of the future. At the poles the earth still tries graciously to shine again. In serious souls, the calling glows to establish the archetypal light in human beings. For the human being conceals the enlightenment, in us the first witness of the light is given; in the cosmos it occurs through the northern aurora. Before our task on the planet is done, it is spiritually certain that all the stars will be moved by the earth, will twine round her as their spiritual centre. For the archetypal sun will radiate out of the human being. Therefore, even at that time, I understood life not as a personal affair, but each existence had to be given a supra-personal assignment, of this I was convinced. We

should not here only learn, but it remains our duty to bring
the earth to herself — that is to say, to her proper light.
She will burn, letting her fiery core dawn into the gleaming
crust. The earth, a dark fruit, already germinates upwards
into a world of blossoming light. Religions begin to glow
in order to bring rebirth to the peoples in the inner fire.
We are responsible that in all activity and events the light
of help shoots up. No chains in being: spontaneity! That
is the resurrection of the body!

Däubler's Protestant parents held radical, free-thinking views,
valuing Darwin's and Haeckel's outlooks very highly. The Catholic
mystical attitude of the work-places in the manor house in Trieste
presented an almost dramatic contrast within the young Däubler's
upbringing. However, this polarity was fruitful. He was nine years
old when he went to school, but could not adjust to it. Following
this, he received private tuition. When he was only fifteen years old,
the young Däubler made a long sea voyage in the Mediterranean as
a ship's boy. His tendency to day-dream was unusually strong. In
this way, Däubler got to know nature in a quite different manner
from all other people; the sun became a god for him, the moon a
dream divinity. Someone told the day-dreaming boy that once the
sun and the earth had been united; together with his particular
interest in physics, geography and history, this information gave rise
in him to an initial synthesis of cosmological events. Däubler also
writes about this in his foreword (1921, 8f):

And the earth itself gives birth to powers which, in
opposition to gravity, desire to return to the sun: I saw in
this the mechanical law through which life arises. Every
plant, every animal, wraps itself up in its flight to the sun.
Indeed, basically, it is not heat, electricity, magnetism, and
so on, that is concerned with soul and bodily growth;
various known and unresearched powers surround us with
sun, moon and star-content. Actually, existence means:
return to the sun.

These thoughts are further turned inwardly in such a manner that
Däubler perceives that all this attains its end in the human being.
This, however, is consciously placed in the earth's night; indeed, he
has, after all, brought forth and willed this night himself as his field
of destiny. Nevertheless, the human being also bears the sun within
himself and thus can reveal the stars to the earth. In this way, the
power of the heavens is unfolded in the earth's darkness. This is lit

up like the sun through humanity. ('You feeble night . . .' in 'Hymn to Venice'). Such evolutionary pictures place the human being actively and with responsibility in the world's stream of becoming. An ever-recurring motive in the action arises from this in the developing epic.

In the course of the epic, Däubler attempts to describe the progress of humanity through the great cultures. India is for him an archetypal state; this portion of humanity comes out of the sun's nature and only strives towards it. The unfulfilled destiny is a tragedy: 'The coulisse of karma makes us shudder' (1921, 14). Yet humanity wanders on. In ancient Persia a turning point was reached: 'Across Iran's starward-pointing heights there is a northerly trend to the spiral of the future, forward-ascending peoples' (1921, 14). On this journey through the cultures, Däubler encounters the Logos working in them, the Christ, and the human 'I' connected thereto.

> The 'I' was always present when a section of the world was
> destroyed. Peoples, who, like individual souls had
> concealed themselves in human form by an existential
> decision see it, the 'I' (as eternally engaged in it), again
> swallowed by the waves of the ancient flood. The Logos
> proclaims its eternity to the 'I' through its very own cry,
> the archaic shout, 'that is what I sought and have found.'
> (1921, 16).

> Jesus Christ has revealed to us the new task; to take
> upon us in this life as a cross that which has come to us,
> our prenatal imperfection, to endure individual suffering in
> holy communities. He solicits the heights of all confessions
> and brings them to us there where he prepared Pentecost.
> The festival in the Spirit! The ancient light's outburst from
> nature can, in the northwards directed homeward journey
> to the pole of calm within us, always become a surprising
> day of festivity. Pentecost fulfils and awaits the one who is
> striding northwards. The northwards thinker. The one who
> suffers the North. (1921, 14f).

For Däubler, the working and being of the Logos-Christ was woven into humanity's journey through the cultures. Even in Egypt, at the time of the Israelite's exodus, he was this being appearing (1921, 17f).

> The ancient call, 'Ra', too, lives eruptively in the minds of
> the Ra-bearing Egyptian people; a king is born,
> Amenophis IV, who perceived the decline of Apis as the

age of Taurus. It had to give way to that of Aries; this is
the moment to have a presentiment of the echoing of the
Logos in the one and only sun god Ra: to break through!
Amenophis IV attempted it. He did not hesitate to make
even Thebes go up in smoke and flames. He did not
succeed in his purpose; his followers betrayed him. But he
certainly fulfilled the deed in spirit!

The epic progress through the cultural ages is seen by Däubler
against the background of changing astral powers. According to his
own testimony, he had often obtained esoteric works. This was
inevitable in view of his extensive search. It is clear from his prose
works that theosophical circles were part of his environment; he
knew the terminology of these circles and used them himself. To
this also belonged the conceptions of stellar influence on human
cultures. Later, he heard about Rudolf Steiner. In her biography of
Michael Bauer (1871–1929), Margareta Morgenstern (1879–1968) the
wife of the poet Christian Morgenstern (1871–1914) gives a short
but characteristic description of Däubler in Munich (about 1918) in
the circle of well-known artists (Morgenstern 1950, 132):

> During a lengthy stay in Munich, Michael Bauer
> participated enthusiastically in the cultural life of the city.
> He now met here Albert Steffen with whom he entered into
> a warm friendship that lasted until the end of his life.
> There, they experienced together the tumultous time of the
> council of People's Delegates and heard many lectures by
> eminent personalities. All these impressions were then
> exchanged at lunch, when they met together with the
> painter and sculptor Hans Wildermann in a vegetarian
> restaurant which Ricarda Huch and Rilke also frequented.
> The Swiss writer Ernst Uehli also belonged to Michael
> Bauer's intimate circle of friends. He was also invited,
> together with Albert Steffen and Michael Bauer, to an
> evening with Steffen's friends, where a fervent discussion
> on Rudolf Steiner took place which brought a very
> significant exclamation from Däubler . . .

Däubler knew about Anthroposophy and had no doubt absorbed it
through the esoteric writings he mentions. In Berlin, during the
winter 1926/27, he had also read from his northern lights epic to a
student circle of the growing Christian Community which arose out
of Anthroposophy as a movement for religious renewal. In a conver-
sation with Dr Horst Lindenberg, the priest of The Christian

Community who had invited him, Däubler affirmed his acquaintance with Anthroposophy but let it be known that he was too busy with lectures and his own writing to be able to occupy himself extensively with Rudolf Steiner's work. The poet started at this time a series of lecture tours and art journeys which carried him through the whole of Europe. At the same time, he began to grow ill, tuberculosis made itself noticeable and Däubler died of it seven years later (1934) at St Blasien in the Black Forest.

Däubler's sense for art was directed not only toward poetry. This became a serious form of expression only after his parents had moved to Vienna and he had the opportunity of hearing a great deal of music, Wagner and Mahler, in that city. According to his own statement, Däubler began after this to think almost only in verse. His relationship to painting was extensive; he also had always hoped to become a painter. During the years when the second part of the northern lights epic was taking form in Paris, 1903–6, he laid the foundations of his future-orientated understanding of modern painting. He then became the eminent promoter of expressionist painting; above all, of the work of Franz Marc (1880–1916).

He also supported sculpture; he was a friend of Ernst Barlach (1870–1938) and contributed significantly towards making this artist known. Barlach met Däubler in Florence where Däubler had gone to live in 1910 during the completion of his *Nordlicht*. In his autobiography Barlach writes of this encounter (1948, 41):

> One fine day, the majestic, weighty incarnation of
> Däubler's astral spirit lay behind the greasy marble tables
> of the cafe Reinighaus, lay there like an exotic ruler
> travelling incognito, although in ambush, hiding in half-
> light from the worry and torment of existence in his cave
> full of life's sad comfort, knowing everything and
> possessing nothing, happy. The twelve years' labour, the
> bringing forth of *Das Nordlicht*, was finished . . . The
> work began to be printed that same summer and it
> happened with marvellous grandeur as Däubler thrust the
> cataract of verses and falling stars from other worlds as an
> indispensable supplement to the whole, into the hands of
> his editor, Moeller van den Bruck.

In his unfinished novel, *Seespeck*, Barlach portrays Däubler's appearance and nature with precise and characteristically colourful words (1956, 2, 448–470):

> Then he himself began to speak like a standard-bearer, as

Figure 22. The Stargazer *(Theodor Däubler). Pen sketch by Ernst Barlach, January 13, 1909.*

though by the grace of God. This standard he planted on far-away visible ramparts somewhere on the crown of a green hillock, because he himself, on this evening, would raise castles, build walls and found altars. All this before the astonished eyes of the other two who had not been prepared for such a spectacle. To this he added a number of passageways below the earth and above the heavens. He thumped with his fist, which was tender and small, and waved a magic wand in the air, and, behold, the world stood still, shrank and formed itself into a geometric picture which he now balanced on the palm of his hand, and, because it was still glowing from the process of shrinking, he let it stand in the air to cool between his thumb and forefinger and in all this he was not hindered by the dark seams of his shirt-cuffs, which hung unfashionably from his sleeves, nor by his dishevelled collar. He handled the world crystal between his finger-tips like a raw egg. It was blown empty and then filled with meaning, and thus he let the new world of his spirit be grasped with hands . . .

'From time to time Däubler, his arms propped up on the table, bent his massive upper-body over the table like a mountain, then the joints creaked as though something was cracking in the world's timbers — then his lips brought the heavy power of his voice up from volcanic depths and his belly seemed to hide a metallic subterranean flood of conviction . . .

In the hotels, Däubler was regarded somewhat like a travelling prince, sometimes almost as one who had escaped from hell accompanied by his paying secretary. Exotic and therefore peculiar. They saw with astonishment how imperiously he walked, how impetuously he sat down, like a slavemaster, accustomed to obedience, shouted for service and consumed everything served up . . . And his talk took the breath away, even for the waiters who stood near him at the ready . . . it had something of the swindler about it.

The first part of *Das Nordlicht* bore the title 'Mediterranean'. Auroral motifs are used directly only in the first sections, 'Prologue', 'Hymn to the Heights', and 'Venice', as an introduction to the whole work. In the following sections impressions of cities, landscapes and cultural situations are described: 'Rome', 'Florence', 'Dream of Venice', 'Pearls of Venice', 'Naples' and 'Panorphic Intermezzo.'

The second part of the epic is entitled 'Sahara'. Of this Däubler says (1921, 19): 'It means the desert solitariness out of which the "I" can radiate in purity, where it actually becomes creative and its being begins to be reborn.' In the second part, too, the northern lights motif appears, at first with the 'Drama of Ra'. Then follows the main title, 'Ararat', by which name Däubler seems to indicate everything that has taken place within humanity in the form of culture since the great Flood, for it was assumed that at this place Noah's ark landed. For the poet, Mount Ararat is both the beginning and the irrevocable past. Leaving and overcoming Ararat is a central motive of the epic. Under the title 'Ararat' are the subheadings, 'Indian Symphony', 'Iranian Rhapsody', 'Alexandrian Phantasy', 'Roland', 'Three Events', 'The Resurrection of the Body', 'Ararat Erupts', 'Songs in the Soul's Gleaming', 'The Flaming Stream of Lava', and 'The Spirit'. In the last section, the northern lights motif appears again, receiving, towards the end, a crowning and concluding appraisal.

150

8. THEODORE DÄUBLER

The contents of both volumes present a gigantic conception which Däubler, despite his treating it all through in terms of periods, is unable to realize. This discrepancy is the weakness of the work. Däubler's destiny reveals him as a man of space whom unremittant travel imbues with sensitivity for the world. The time element caused him difficulties. `A thoroughgoing meaningful connection between the individual sections could not, therefore, be attained. On the other hand, each sentence of the many thousand verses bears the stamp of a reality hardly to be found in any other poetry. Däubler adds breadth to the soul's spatial mood in his poetry and forms it into a comprehensive spiritual-physical reality. It is, therefore, with justification that Friedhelm Kemp, in the epilogue to the Däubler works (1956) writes:

> It would, indeed, be more illuminating to trace the
> ancestors of Däubler's spirit-light doctrine through
> Western philosophy and mysticism back to Platonism.
> Here, it must suffice to consider the immediate subject-
> matter and to point out that, in *Das Nordlicht* we have, in
> the end, nothing other than a belated crowning of German
> idealism. Who else, among German poets, can claim to be
> the future's awaited genius expressed by Schelling in the
> introduction to his *Weltalter*, he 'who sings the greatest
> heroic poem, comprehensive in spirit, extolled by seers in
> prehistoric times, what was, what is and what will be?'
> These coherences which are confirmed in many of the
> stanzas of the epic were first indicated by Carl Schmitt . . .

It is not surprising, therefore, that the people of Trieste, at an early date, called Däubler the 'Dante of Trieste'. It was a friend of Däubler's who published a first edition of the epic with 750 copies: Moeller van den Bruck (1876–1925), an art historian and also political writer who, together with Dmitry Merezhkovski (1865–1941) published the works of Fyodor Dostoyevksy (1821–81). Even the poorest of the Parisian artists contributed subscriptions to this first edition of *Das Nordlicht* in order that it would be sure to appear.

The perception of the aurora in the darkness of the planet earth meant, for Däubler, the sign of a way which humanity on earth will take. Through his penetration into the cultural periods he had recognized that the way of humanity led slowly northwards. The human being was born of the sun; he had a tropical destiny which is taken up in his inner being and worked upon. In this wandering,

151

the human being needs the darkness of the earth; only here do the star worlds appear to him, conveying eternal wisdom. At a particular phase of his wandering the aurora appeared to the human being. It is the miracle of sun and earth's procreation. For Däubler, the aurora was the procreated flower of the earth which he experienced as a living being in every phase of his life and poetry. The auroral wreaths appearing as blossoms had, therefore, to be the goal of the earth and of human beings. In connection with this the tensions in humanity will be released, and this will, for example, draw the races together; thus follows the pentecostal experience of the aurora (1921, 21).

You surmise the collapse of racial centres into one another;
The golden and the white peoples are reconciled
And offer the secrets of their being to the stars:
Through stars of youth the grey land will be spared!

Däubler knew, however, that humanity's wandering has by no means yet arrived in the sphere of the aurora. In the first place, it will be the task of individuals to realize what has been envisioned (1921, 36).

The path through the ice to the 'I' in God will be the task
of individuals; whoever masters the northern lights as a
cosmic phenomenon among us on earth, and at the same
time sees it as the innermost freedom, will bring it to the
others. Thus the northern lights attained by the spirit
belong to all creatures of the earth. A moon should break
forth, but the youngest sun comes! We are not turning back
to the ancient light, but the ancient light comes through
us to the world. Its buried glimmer can be brought back
to the stars only by human beings. Stars and hierarchies
await it.'

It belongs to Däubler's peculiar destiny that he always sought in vain for a book giving more exact information about the aurora. Such a book could not exist at that time, and so Däubler had to acquire his knowledge by other means. We can see today how surprisingly exact in all details his knowledge of the outer and inner nature of the northern lights was. Däubler was always able to describe the aurora in new words and from ever-new aspects.

In the progress of the second poem of the prologue ('I Saw hereafter in a Rainbow'), the aurora description begins with a consideration of the cause of the heavenly phenomenon: the earth bears this cause as an impulse of the sun within itself; through this it is active

and overcomes the crust of rock in order to produce light. This light
enlightens the threatening apathy of the earth.

> Now the things of heaven fundamentally I know:
> The earth bears in its core the sun's command!
> At the call of light the ring of rock bursts,
> And what was inert shows itself in flaming gold.

The gift of the sun's being is considered a few stanzas later. The
unity of sun and earth is experienced in the empty ice-fields of the
earth. Out of this unity, the earth brings forth the northern lights'
bowl (the oval), and rejuvenates the world thereby, (somewhat as
the flowers in spring rejuvenate the year). This blossoming of the
earth is reflected in the cosmos: the earth — through the aurora, a
star — greets other stars. 'Thus a jubilant salutation blossoms from
star to star.'

The third poem in the prologue imparts in its entirety a broad
picture of the spiritual relationships of the earth to human beings
and the sun in the light of the aurora. In the second verse the flames
of this light become glowing activators which are seen as the earth's
gardener. The treasures of the earth's depths are revealed. Pilgrim
workers bring it about that 'the one believed dead', the human
being, and also the Christ is resurrected. In this way, human beings
become generators of the northern lights, a conception which often
arises with Däubler. As an image of the soul it is comprehensible:
the human being generates spiritual light as the earth does the
aurora. Whether and to what degree this human light participates in
the formation of the aurora in the detour over the earth's etheric
energy-sphere is only to be established by future research into the
northern lights. In the above-mentioned poem, Däubler assumes that
human beings already exist who wander in the aurora's flame
garden. This apocalyptic trait permeates the whole of the epic, it is
the proclamation: it will be and is already present. Here, already, at
the beginning of the epic the aim is clearly revealed: the human
being unites with the earth in the light; only here does he find the
future, sunlike nature.

Towards the end of the whole epic, in the last quarter of the
second volume, there is a section entitled 'Three Events;' it is the
kernel of the epic and has autobiographical over tones. In the foreword of the epic Däubler writes of this (1921, 29): 'Then I wanted
rather to have the secret between all these events made known . . .
and I speak unwillingly here of the actual meaning of this last section
of my epic in terms of the veils of maya'.

A limping, medieval scholar from Germany is at the centre of the colourful, tumultuous, though tragic, events. The previous section is called 'Roland' and describes the destiny of this figure. This Roland had penetrated to the hidden Grail. Däubler goes on to write about this figure.

> The romantic Roland . . . still had to drag a blood-descendant through the misery of the earth, before the abolute 'I' . . . could reach the ultimate insight, and speak unconditionally, overriding all experience. Only after the 'Three Events' . . . should the northern lights shine forth clearly from an 'I'.

With this 'I' through which the aurora rays out clearly in poetical form Däubler speaks of himself. But he preferred to keep 'the secret hidden'. The poet describes the wandering scholar as a revealing picture of his own individuality, as 'absolute I'. Thus the following events and results of the epic are of the 'ultimate insight' and are expressed absolutely, 'overriding all experience'.

Three spinning maidens appear before the wandering scholar in France on the River Rhône at midday. Like meditating goddesses of fate, they lead the coming tableau of destiny through their being. Immediately afterwards, three Cathar knights appear; upon asking the origin of the scholar, he answers: 'A wandering scholar from the land of the barbarians and also an untiring Christian! . . . The sod itself gave birth to my kind of faith. Christ's flame greens and blossoms on every leaf.' After an intensive investigation of the knights' nature, the scholar withstands the temptation to attach himself to the fascinating spirituality of the Cathars.

Soon after this, the wanderer enters an inn in the same region in order to carouse with a soldier of fortune and a prostitute. In the background come haunting stories of the devil. When knights of St John, 'Defender of damned Popes', appear in front of the inn they are for no reason thrown down and killed by the scholar and the soldier. Nevertheless, following this deed, the scholar again resists the temptation to become a serf. In a neighbouring forest, the wanderer experiences a ghostly witches' vigil. Some time later he meets a recluse with a red beard and red hair; he is a giant with sky-blue eyes. The scholar follows him into his cave and receives various kinds of instruction about mankind's ever increasingly difficult journey to the North, and about Christ who 'from the beginning glowed in the earth's night'. After this instruction, the scholar goes on his way and then finds himself in the vicinity of Speyer in

8. THEODORE DÄUBLER

Germany. The witches' sabbath which for a long time ever and again came into his thoughts, here becomes reality. It ends with the arrest of the scholar who is burnt at the stake. The shadow of his double, from whom he had always expected protection, was fatigued and had given him up. Concerning this end, Däubler writes in the introduction (1921, 29f):

> The last section of the 'Three Events' takes place entirely contemporaneously, internally within the absolute 'I' and in this world under human conditions. The 'Three Events' are hair-raising, appearing finally quite vacuous with reference to the ultimate aims of the 'I'. This scholar, an impetuous person, should not indulge in the pleasures of women; that is his metaphysical mission! He struggles in frustration for love and also for lust. Destiny is stronger; at the moment of his love-affair with a witch he is seized by bailiffs, actually without reason, and burnt.
>
> The 'I', the Adam is Ararat, must work itself out as karma demands in apocalyptic forms in which, nevertheless, its visions are brought to expression on other worldly levels.

And now, as a conclusion to the 'Three Events', Däubler describes what this unveiling 'I' experiences in the scholar's incineration:

> Shock. The fire is choking in the volcano!
> I am lying in the pit being burned.
> In the throat of Ararat sabbath, companions are roasting,
> And I am banned deep in the Tartarus.
>
> But soon you will display no more ostentation, you last of
>   Titans!
> The crater buries the growing wall round about.
> In death, earth's suffering is immediately forgotten:
> I can barely contain the pain of the burning wounds,
> In dying, I had had the presumption to believe,
> That the soul, like a dove, flew away from realms of space.
> But no, between the cliffs of Ararat and its passes,
> I am still aware of the most inward dream.

This concluding vision 'as karma demands', is still in the past. It is completely transformed in the transition to the next section of the epic, 'The Resurrection of the Body', and becomes the unveiling future which bears within it a surmounted and enlightened past. It appears in full clarity in the introductory 'Apocalypse':

My grave is no pyramid,
My grave is a volcano!
The northern lights shine out in full song,
The night is already subject to me!
This peace is irksome to me,
I sacrifice delusion for freedom!
The artificiality by which we uphold ourselves,
My fire will split Ararat!

Though Adam be carried to his grave,
His worldly instinct remains behind
Built up of a thousand marble legends:
I alone, a shadow, limping to work,
Am only able to complain bitterly about the ancestor,
Because he struggles in the pit for self-command through
                me.
The grave which he builds up for himself in his faith
That transcience will never rob him of his archetype!

I feel, proud earthly father,
Your suffering that broke open the laws:
You are thinking a drama in the theatre,
That presses on you thousandfold.
You breathe freedom from the crater,
Which contracts terribly:
Endeavour to renounce your sepulchral peace,
Then your heart's star will lighten the world!

I myself am a spark of freedom,
I cannot tolerate stability!
Away with the pomp of experience,
I can do without a grave!
Grace foams in the drink of the ancient fire
As excess in the last judgment;
However I will keep it with my shadow,
I dream you, freed powers of the earth!

8. THEODORE DÄUBLER

My grave is no pyramid,
My grave is a volcano.
My brain is a smithy of sparks,
May the work of conversion be done!
No peace rings from cheerful song,
My will shall become a world hurricane.
My breath will create lucid forms of day,
Which, barely seen, will split Ararat asunder!

In the sequel of this section of the epic a link is made with the dramatic original happening of the 'Apocalypse'; there is described the Tartarus, the volcanic region of the underworld, with its activity. The human being awakens here under a curtained sky. Gone is piety, the sun's commands die away. However, the glow of inwardness is born! The aurora, as inner experience, rises up out of the abyss, but does not, as yet, lead into the heights. Instead, enigmas are solved and the human being announces to himself the tidings that the originating spirit has chosen humanity. The darkness will shortly leave the underworld, the storm fly from the northern seas. The inner shining of Jesus' birth star will spread across the sky.

In the following section, 'Songs in the Soul's Shining', the manifold effects of the moon are described in the poem, 'Full Moon'. In the spiritual moonshine, the heart's experience of humanity rises silvery from the meadows. In the aurora-forests veiled brides are surprised; around humanity a mighty perception arises during which all the beings of the North strive to become visible.

Experiences of the heart rise argentine around the pastures.
The veiled brides stand wondering in auroral groves.
An overwhelming vision embraces you,
With all the northern spirits seeking to appear.

This description is continued also in the poem, 'New Moon': the aurora is flaming in order to lead the glow on into the night. This brings the day out of itself, in which the flaming of the truth raises memories of the Omnipotent One. The old moon has died. The earth can generate new moons. It has brought forth the Son from its centre. He is followed by the child from the heights (Rev.12), surrounded by thoughts. The night has become a transparent, unique day. The human body is liberated, its death outlasts the death of common death. Human sleep gives the dream to death. The obdurate experiences itself full of anxiety in the debris of glaciers; in the pale ice the planet earth lies in a trance, producing thereby the truth of all worlds. The planet earth is bright! Now it goes its way in freedom. Siberia's interior brings forth the calm, frozen aurora; mountains of light flame up and move spontaneously of their own accord. This sky, generated by the earth, will not be lost to any world.

In the epic section before the last 'The Flaming Lava Stream', in the poem 'The Blind One' the gradations of sound of the auroral experience are delineated. The barely audible 'snorting' of the northern lights is transformed into singing on the detour through dream; finally, it issues out of all things and thereby overcomes the materiality of existence. The Word arises, the world-light sounds and lifts itself into the space of the stars. The aurora's substance overcomes objects from within. In the arising grandeur, the human being hears himself, becomes blinder, but with more sensitive feelings. Access to the timeless origin is open to him; the foundation of the world is no longer troubled by measurement that only leads to consciousness of objects: the world is the way of the flaming sky.

The motif of silence appears in the poem, 'The Sleeper'. An account is often given of the immeasurable silence of the polar night. Against this undisturbed background of silence the northern lights appear in particularly spiritual resounding glory. The aurora arises out of sleep and waking (it is related to dream and for its proper perception demands indeed the greatest wakefulness). The aurora reveals the deeper being of the cosmic bodies of the worlds. It seeks to awaken the human being and lead him into sunlike vision; it bridges gaps in consciousness. The human being is looked at by the aurora; his response is love. The northern lights have reached their aim when the human being goes to sleep in self-forgetfulness: he may then live in the innocence of the azure day.

The northern lights bring silence. The northern lights lower
    the eyelids.
The northern lights waft in you and surge over you,
For a world sinks gloriously down to you.

The northern lights, the son of two sun-born suns
(For slumber and consciousness have created them.)
They set, in brightness, sun, moon and stars upon the
    throne.

So, in you, the northern lights will snatch away the night.
They see the suns, reveal the suns, generate the suns.
The northern lights rise up where the shafts of consciousness
      gape open.

The northern lights look upon you, entangled they glow
      within you.
You love them graciously, they will be comforted in you:
You sleep. If you forget yourself, then the glow has won:

And soon the day will dawn, innocent and pure.

A section of 'The Flaming Lava Stream' bears the title, 'Wind to the Home'. In the poem 'The Blind Midwife', Däubler speaks of the appearance of new prophets of the future on the earth. They will be there suddenly, bringing enlightenment to great parts of the earth with their talents. At the same time, old paths will no longer be traversable and for this reason fear will take hold of humanity. The world will be renewed in humanity: illusions will be seen through and the human being will come to himself. Sorrows will be transformed into morning gold. In the depths of life the aurora light will shine, during which the human being will have taken the world up into his day. Stars will subdue the darkening force of ecstacy, for they are the guardians of direction.

    'The Magic Song' is also a part of the 'Flaming Lava Stream' Here, the aurora appears as a threatening apparition. The human being experiences himself in God, but the unknown forces of nature — the aurora, too — could overpower him terribly in their alienation. Among the primitive peoples of the polar regions, this terrible fear of the blood-red, lit-up dark sky continually descended upon them. In Däubler's poetic knowledge the coming fear of destiny is revealed; already, as Perseus, he has separated himself from the divine world, however, in its being the guarantee of a healing return is given.

Oh God, I am in God! I can already grasp God's world!
What threatens me now? I am afraid. Flames penetrate my
      faith:
A red apparition of the night appears and penetrates me, to
      hate.
It goes around in the North and appears to originate in the
      glaciers!

The red, terrible apparition in the North calls within me:
'Your spirit, as Perseus, broke away already from the
         mountains!
It had become the steep expression of this nightly star
And seemed called upon to assure our flight to the Lord.'

In the section 'Flaming Stream of Lava' there appear a number of poems containing auroral themes, among which is the poem 'Northern Shimmer'. The remaining poems of *Das Nordlicht* which directly concern the aurora are given in full in the German edition of this book. In an essay of 1931 (published posthumously in 1956), the thinker Däubler gathers together the whole conception of the basic elements in the epic, *Das Nordlicht*, and fits them together into a cosmic-earthly and Christian world conception.

> The spiritual sun still remains sun: a hell of passion boils in its wreath of flames. The flames are allayed by the *sun-god* among the Elohim, our Saviour Jesus Christ, so that they do not spread out into the universe. Received into the sun of his illustriousness from the earliest time, he is born into the realm of the daily sun. Thus has he blessed the earth, for ever linked to the sun in man, to the sun of song in whose centre the *archetypal light* of the creator holds sway, that neither rays forth nor stings. The sun of song stands in the equilibrium of the spirit to the silence of the pole surrounded by the ice-hemmed earth, as the innermost archetypal light to the northern lights glimmering over the world.
>
> The *Son of Man* is the sun in the Spirit. He guides us to his vineyard which needs our care. The ancient brotherhood of all creatures is disclosed to the One who is well-disposed. Simplified, we shall find ourselves again. Unnamed rays from the earth, unseen from the stars, will watch over and transform the circumstances of the living. But our death is coming. We are our own stranglers. However, the Lord is with the living. Where the earth grows inert, the northern brightness pervades the night. There, a comet breaks in from seeds in order to swirl through the darkness. *The northern lights are a mark of the pentecostal flame.* To the heads of peoples it means, therefore, propitiation in the cold light, of which it is said, it is the original source before the inflamed creation. The

northern lights promise: The earth will one day out of itself become a radiant star. The northern lights proclaim: The speck of dust, earth, will become the spark of freedom in the universe. This wish, coming from the dark star, will never be realized in the world of phenomena: it is to be realized in the spirit. The creation was made to this end, to this end was man born. The Son of Man will remain among us so that the Spirit may come to rule. Quivering northern light above the mountains of ice indicate that the pentecostal flames fade into the dusk through the peoples. If enlightenment comes to a human being then in tongues a peony will become visible in the polar night to the walker over the glaciers. The inner sun dawns as inner brightness: Northern brightness gives rise to reverence in the creature, unites us to peace, promotes freedom in humanity.

The concluding poetry of the epic begins with the sentences: 'The earth is burning! Extinguished are the chimneys of the fire shafts. Dead is the volcano, exterminated is the evil that threatened us in fire!' The first statement on the burning fire concerns the new fire, the blaze from above which the aurora helps to generate. It stands in contrast to the old fire, the earthly fire from below. This is, at the same time, the human past. The future is the fire of the universe which the human being, in regarding the aurora, begins to grow into. He is no longer dependent upon the deep powers of the old earth fire.

In the middle of this poem the being of the aurora is once again revealed in conclusion. It is mild, veil-like fire; the original order of the sound of language comes forth from it. It is thus the new-arriving world word. The world's favourite son is the human being; he will attain to the externally great by also discovering the auroral gold that springs from the earth. Independent of bodily existence, the human being can take upon himself a different soul-life. The auroral flames of timeless life are united with the stars. We must turn to these flames and hold them fast on their way into the sky, for we need their heat. Human beings and other beings will themselves become burning doors of heaven and flaming meteors. Then the aurora can and will disappear.

In this future, human beings will find themselves again in the spirit and will remain in the spirit; the aurora unites man and man with the spirit. There follows as a conclusion to the book the promised verse of this last of Theodor Däubler's poems in *Das Nordlicht*.

The veil of fire that mildly runs through us,
Has no more thunder-words in its lap,
Each sound springs forth as an ordering member.

The earth burns. Invulnerable to the red thrust
Out of the underworld, whence the auroral gold exudes,
Its favourite son attains eternal greatness!

O flames that give eternal life to us,
Denying the body, I can quaff the soul,
You are the spark that loves the stars.

You still fly about the pole in centrifugal fling,
From the earth's heart into space above,
But remain in us who need the fire!

Once, heaven's gates will burn in me.
Auroral lights will disappear from the firmament
For each being is a fiery meteor.

Then we will find the other world within us,
Where no-one emerges from the spirit-ocean,
Aurora borealis can unite us with the spirit.

Bibliography

Akasofu, Syuin-Ichi. 1979. 'Aurora borealis — the amazing northern lights'. *Alaska Geography* 6. Anchorage: Northwest.

Aristotle. 1910–30. *Meteorologica*. Oxford: Clarendon.

Barlach, Ernst. 1948. *Ein selbsterzähltes Leben*. München: Piper.

——. 1956. *Das dichterische Werk*. München: Piper.

Brekke, A., & A. Egeland. 1979. *Nordlyset, Fra mytologi til romforskning*. Oslo: Grondahl.

Bühler, Walther. 1972–7. *Goethe in unserer Zeit*. Dornach: Philosophisch-Anthroposophisch.

Carrington, Richard C. 1860. 'Description of a singular appearance yseen in the sun . . .' *Monthly Notices of the Royal Astronomical Society*. 20. London.

Crottet, R. 1963. *Nordlicht*, Hamburg: Christian Wegner.

Däubler, Theodor. 1921. *Das Nordlicht*. [Genfer Ausgabe]. Leipzig: Insel.

——. 1956. *Dichtung und Schriften*, München: Kösel.

Eather, R. H. 1980. *Majestic Lights*, Washington: American Geophysical Union.

Evans, J. V. 1982. April 30. 'The Sun's Influence on the Earth's Atmosphere and Interplanetary Space.' *Science*. Washington: American Association for the Advancement of Science.

Gromnica, E. 1971. 'An unbelievable story about the northern lights.' *North/Nord*. Ottawa: Department of Indian & Northern Affairs.

Gustafsson, G. 1982. *Physikalische Blatter*, No. 38. Weinheim: Deutsche Physikalische Gesellschaft.

Halley, Edmund. 1717. 'An Account of the late surprizing Appearance of the *Lights* seen in the *Air*'. *Philosophical Transactions of the Royal Society*, No. 347. London.

Hamilton, J. C. 1903. 'The Algonquin Nanabozho and Hiawatha.' *American Folklore*. No. 16. Boston, Mass.

Hawkes, Ernest W. 1916. 'The Labrador Eskimo', Mem. 91, *Geological Survey of Canada*, Ottowa: Government Printing Bureau.

Holweger, H. 1982 summer. *Pressemitteilungen*. Kiel: Astrophysikalische Forschungsgruppe.

Judson, Katherine B. 1920. *Myths and Legends of the Pacific Northwest*. Chicago: A. C. McClurg.

Kalevala, The Land of Heroes, 1977. Trans. W. F. Kirby. London: Dent.

King's Mirror, The, [Konungs Skuggsjá]. 1917. Trans. Laurence M. Larson. New York: American-Scandinavian, and London: Oxford.

Lomonosov, Michail, 1747. *Rhetoric*.

Macculloch, C. J. A. (Ed). 1927. *Mythology of all Races*. Boston.

Morgenstern, Margareta. 1950. *Michael Bauer — ein Burger zweier Welten*. München: Piper.

Nansen, Fridtjof. 1904. *Furthest North*, London: Constable.

Paulsen, A. 1896. 'Nordlysets Straalingsteori'. *Nyt Tidsskrift for Fysik og Kemi*. København.

Payer, J. 1876. *Die österreichisch-ungarische Nordpol-Expedition*. Wien.

Plutarch. 1952. *Lysander*, in *Plutarch's Lives*, Cambridge, Mass.: Harvard.

Pontoppidan, E. 1751–53. *Det første forsøc paa Norges Naturlige Historie*.

Rasmussen, Knud. 1929. 'Intellectual Culture of the Iglulik Eskimos'. *Fifth Thule Expedition*. København: Glydem Dalski.

Ray, Dorothy J. 1958 July. *Alaska Sportsman*. Anchorage: Northwest.

Scott, Robert F. 1927. *Scott's Last Expedition*, London: Murray.

Seneca, 1972. *Naturales Questiones*; Cambridge, Mass.: Harvard; and London: Heinemann.

Siscoe, G. L. 1978. 'A historical footnote on the origin of aurora borealis'. *EOS Trans. AGU* 59, 994.

——, & Wang. *see* Wang, P. K.

Steiner, Rudolf. 1953. *The Inner Realities of Evolution*, London: Steiner.

——. 1979. *Occult Science. An Outline*. London: Steiner.

Taylor, Bayard, 1864. *The Prose Writings of Bayard Taylor*. New York: Putnam.

Tromholt, Sophus. 1885. *Under the Rays of the Northern Lights*. London.

Unsöld, A. 1955. *Physik der Sternatmosphären*. Berlin: Springer.

Wachsmuth, Günther, 1965. *Erde und Mensch*. Dornach: Philosophisch-Anthroposophisch.

Wang, P. K., & G. L. Siscoe, 1979. *Some early descriptions of auroras in China*. Los Angeles.

Index

INDEX